The Illustrated Library of
NATURE

VOLUME 5

DESERT
LIFE

DUNE
LIFE

The American Museum of Natural History

Cooperated in the publication of this edition.

The opinions expressed by authors are their own and do not necessarily reflect the policy of the Museum.

The Illustrated Library of
NATURE

*T*HIS PICTORIAL ENCYCLOPEDIA of natural history and ecology depicts the relationships of all living organisms to each other and between them and their environments. Original manuscript from the *Doubleday Nature Programs* plus new articles and illustrations are included in this edition.

H. S. STUTTMAN CO., INC., Publishers
New York, N. Y., 10016

Contents

VOLUME 5

(right)
The **saguaros** can grow into grotesque shapes. This further adds to their strangeness.

(below, left)
Named after the Gila River in Arizona, the **Gila woodpecker** is at home among the big saguaro cacti. It bores for insects in the saguaro and also makes a hole in the cactus to nest in.

(below, right)
Many wild animals become accustomed to lights and, like the **mule deer** at the Sonoran Desert Museum at Tucson, Arizona, will come to feed or drink under floodlights.

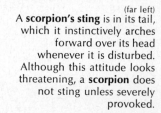

(far left)
A **scorpion's sting** is in its tail, which it instinctively arches forward over its head whenever it is disturbed. Although this attitude looks threatening, a **scorpion** does not sting unless severely provoked.

(left)
Much of Central Asia is desert or semidesert. There the **two-humped camel** plays the same role as its one-humped relative, the Arabian camel, does in southwestern Asia and northern Africa.

R OUGHLY ONE-FOURTH of the earth's land surface is desert, counting the cold deserts such as Antarctica and the icecap of Greenland along with the arid regions of the more temperate zones. These areas are all characterized by sparse vegetation and by extreme shortage of water for use by plants and animals. Generally there is less than ten inches of annual rainfall, distributed erratically over a region and unevenly throughout the seasons and years. The surface—if not ice—may vary from shifting sand to parched earth or fissured lava; it may be flat, sloping or broken up by mountains and bluffs.

Throughout the ages deserts have presented a challenge to the people who have made their homes in them, gone on expeditions to them or merely tried to cross them. Plants and animals that have struggled—and learned—to survive in these harsh, inhospitable environments have had to overcome the same problems. The next three chapters explore the terrain and conditions conquered by these hardy forms of life and the special types of behavior or structural modifications that enable them to live where they do.

Real desert inhabitants—those that can withstand the shortage of water, extremes of temperature and violent winds—are the subjects of DESERT LIFE. This chapter focuses especially on general adaptions by plants for resisting, evading, withstanding or escaping drought and on particular adaptions to desert conditions by animals ranging from camels and kangaroo rats to sand grouse, lizards and insects.

There are few sights more lovely or exalting to the spirit than that of a desert landscape brightened by flowers, and in WILD FLOWERS OF THE DESERT this triumph over hardship and unfavorable conditions is amply recorded and illustrated. Water is vital for plant life, and this chapter considers in depth the kinds of plants that can survive in arid environments and how they cope with the scarcity of water.

CACTUS, the final chapter in this category, is devoted to the strange, drought-resistant plants that were once confined to the New World and which symbolize the desert to many people. These plants well deserve a section of their own, for there are over a thousand species of cacti, occurring in a fantastic variety of shapes and producing some of the most vivid and colorful flowers found anywhere.

DESERT LIFE

► *Varieties of plant and animal life that exist in areas with extremes in temperature.*

Desert Life

O N A MAP OF NORTH AFRICA there is a large area marked "Sahara", stretching from the Atlantic in the west to the Red Sea in the east, the largest desert in the world. The Sahara desert conjures up pictures of endless stretches of burning sand thrown into undulating dunes. Here and there small groups of Bedouin Arabs are to be seen with their camels making for oases, the lush, fertile islands in the seas of sand. This picture of emptiness and bareness is encouraged by the empty space on the map marking the desert. The names of principal oases are marked, otherwise nothing, not even contours.

Now that more people are going into the desert areas the blank spaces on the maps are being filled in by the cartographers. Geologists are looking for oil and minerals and scientists are studying the animals and plants to find how they are able to survive in these apparently uninhabitable places. The answers may help man to open up the deserts for agriculture. If this is possible it will mean that the deserts, which now cover one-quarter of the earth's land surface, will be able to support the world's increasing population.

If you look at the map showing the world's deserts you will see that deserts are to be found all over the world, although most of them lie in a belt running to either side of the equator. The picture of a desert as a stretch of burning sand is only true for one kind of desert. For example, there are cold as well as hot deserts. The cold deserts are such as the continent of Antarctica and the icecap of Greenland. Then there are other deserts that are hot in summer and cold in winter, like the Gobi desert where the cold, bitter winter

In the vast arid plains of the earth's desert regions, the wonderful power of nature to adapt is particularly striking. Where food and water are scarce, the problems of survival are met in ingenious new ways. Throughout the centuries desert animals have developed a variety of survival techniques: the camel endures for long periods without water, the jerboa develops its own air-conditioning system. Some animals stay out of the sun and do their hunting at night. Plants grow thicker leaves or spines to slow down water evaporation. In tropical America the adaptable **iguana** (top right), is able to enjoy any habitat that will provide sufficient green leaves and fruit to nourish it.

Robert J. Lee

While some **deserts** are created naturally by **climatic conditions,** others are the result of **man's misuse of the land** over many centuries. In the Sierra Nevada of Spain, soil erosion is probably the result of both of these factors.

lasts nine months. Even the hot deserts like the Sahara are very cold at night as the heat that was absorbed by the sand during the day radiates off into the clear air after sunset.

Throughout the different kinds of desert there is one continuing feature that makes them barren wastes. There is a lack of water or, rather, a lack of water readily available for use by plants and animals. Deserts are usually found where there is little rainfall, but this does not mean there is no water in such places. The Antarctic continent is a true desert in that there is little precipitation, in the form of snow, but it is covered by water, in the form of ice. The icecap is several thousand feet thick but, being frozen solid, it cannot be used by living things. The Antarctic desert only blooms around the fringes of the continent where the sun is strong enough to melt the ice and let small plants and animals survive.

The Sahara, strangely enough, also has its supplies of water. Although rain comes infrequently and soon soaks away into the dry sand, there are vast reserves of water under the surface. Some of these consist of underground "reservoirs" of water that have been trapped there for millions of years or have flowed there, underground, from outside the desert. These reservoirs are of little use to the inhabitants of the desert except where they come to the surface, as at oases. The only organisms that can get water from below the soil are some plants that have very deep roots, and certain termites. Other plants can absorb dew that forms at night on their leaves and some of the animals lick dew from the leaves. The remaining animals must obtain water by eating succulent plants or live entirely without drinking or go for long periods without drinking.

The sparsity of vegetation in desert areas means that there will

(left)
Few deserts in the world seem more formidable than that of **Arabia.** In a peninsula with an area of about a million square miles, only a small corner receives enough rain to make cultivation feasible, and the salinity of the soil further reduces its productivity. Apart from some mountains and highlands, the landscape is made up of steppe and desert, some tracts of which are sand and others volcanic. Vegetation is extremely sparse, leaving the surface exposed to further erosion, extremes of temperature and high winds.

(right)
Thousands of years ago a million-ton meteor crashed here in the Arizona Desert in an area now called **Meteor Crater.** The crater is three quarters of a mile in diameter and over 500 feet deep.

be large amounts of bare soil exposed to the elements, so leading to erosion, and consequently increasing the barrenness of the desert. Even when rain does fall the first drops from a rainstorm merely cake the surface of the ground, so that the rest of the rain runs over the surface. As there is little vegetation to hold the soil in place the streams of water scour channels and the soil is washed away. At night the temperature of the soil drops rapidly and rocks and pebbles that have expanded during the day contract and crack. Gradually they break up into minute particles to form sand. High winds, also characteristic of deserts where there are no windbreaks, cause sandstorms, and the driven sand blasts the remaining rocks, wearing them away and hastening their destruction.

This, however, is the picture presented by the most barren of deserts. It would be wrong to think of a desert consisting of nothing but sand, rock and occasional plants. There is no definite boundary between lush pastures and completely arid desert. Between the two there is a gradual change, from green fertile lands to semi-arid grassland with sparse vegetation which becomes sparser until finally the only vegetation left is the tough, thorny bushes or the cacti. Where the desert actually begins is often a matter of opinion. Also there are oases dotted about even the driest regions, wherever there are springs, or there will be fertile river banks, as along the Nile or Niger, where rivers flow through deserts.

The fact that there are oases which offer reasonable opportunities for sustaining life in animals as well as man, and that the desert grades so easily into semi-deserts makes for difficulty in defining what is a desert animal. The hyena and vulture of Africa and the rabbit of Australia, for instance, will go into desert or semi-desert areas, but only for a short time. They have no special adaptations enabling them to live in these extreme conditions but they may go into the desert to feed, perhaps pressed by competition from their fellows. Similarly, birds and beasts of prey which normally live in non-desert habitats may go into deserts in search of easy prey.

We are more concerned here with the real desert inhabitants, animals which have so evolved that they can withstand or avoid the acute shortage of water, extremes of temperature and violent winds, all of which add up to a very inhospitable environment. As the conditions are the same for all kinds of desert animals, we shall find that as we discuss them the same adaptations occur in a diversity of species. Many desert animals have the ability to store water in their bodies. To utilize a scattered food supply they are capable of rapid movement from one place to another, and to avoid extremes of temperature many seek shelter underground where they will be out of the sun. In the following pages we shall see that recent research has shown how these protective mechanisms work, how animals with very different body forms, such as snakes, scorpions, rodents and the like,

Bowing toward the East, Muslims pray at sundown in the **Egyptian desert.** Among the inhabitants of this area are the Bedouin, herdsmen making the best adjustment they can to the inhospitable desert conditions. They move from oasis to oasis, seeking pasture wherever grass grows.

(left)
Where water occurs near the surface in an arid region, **lush vegetation** will spring up. Here in the Kibya-Ghadames **oasis** in the Libyan desert a water hole is encircled by palm trees.

are adapted in their bodily form or function so that the internal workings of the body are hardly affected by the adverse conditions of their environment.

Desert Plants

FROM WHAT WE HAVE SEEN of conditions in the deserts, there are bound to be many problems for plant life. Sudden floods may uproot them and sandstorms may bury them or strip their leaves and their bark, but, as with all desert life, the main hazard is a shortage of water. This is a problem that plants everywhere often have to cope with. Even fertile, temperate regions become "deserts" in winter when the water in the soil freezes. Deciduous trees cut down their water loss in winter by shedding their leaves, for plants take up water through their roots, then lose it by evaporation through small holes, called *stomata*, in their leaves. This flow of water through the

(above)
Soil erosion can be caused by **climatic forces,** or it may be brought about by **overgrazing,** especially by goats. Many animals only nibble the top leaves in grazing, but goats eat down to the roots, making the soil less stable. Then winds carry away the soil, exposing the roots of trees, as shown here.

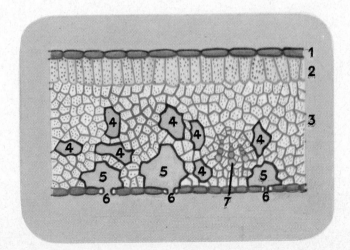

(left)
After absorbing water through their roots, plants lose it through tiny holes in their leaves, called **stomata** (6). Within the tissue of the leaf are lacunae, or cavities (4) and also chambers (5) that lead to the stomata. The epidermis (1) covers the palisade cells (2). The leaf's nerve and its chambers also lie within the interior tissue (7).

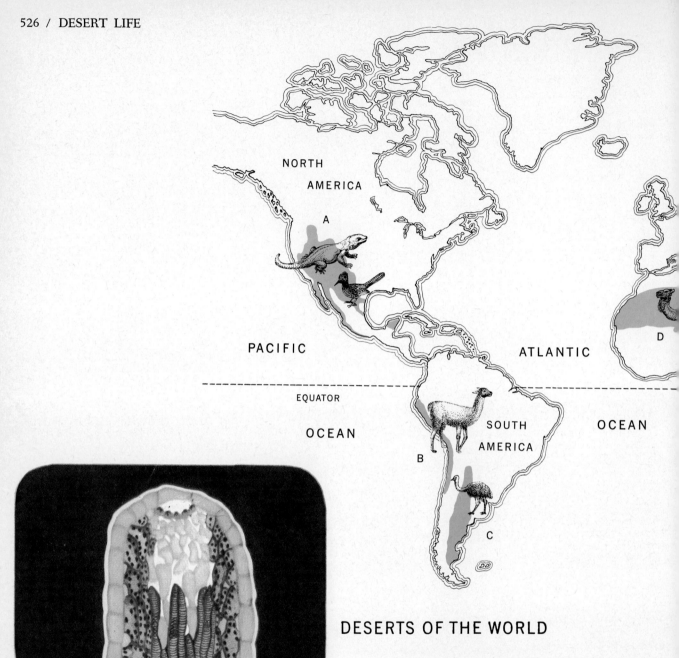

(above)
The **thick, rounded leaves** of many desert plants have small surface areas, thus reducing the volume of evaporation. Sometimes the surface area is protected by a waxlike cuticle.

DESERTS OF THE WORLD

In general, the deserts of the world lie in two belts of moderate latitude, one on each side of the equator. They occur where the prevailing winds are very dry, usually having lost their moisture as rainfall in other upwind areas.

plant is essential to its life, but in the desert the flow must be kept to a minimum.

Even when the desert soil appears parched and most of the plants have withered away, some will still appear green. These are the plants with access to a water supply not available to all. In Death Valley, California, a desert within a desert, where there is no surface water except an occasional short run of bitter salt water, and rainfall averages

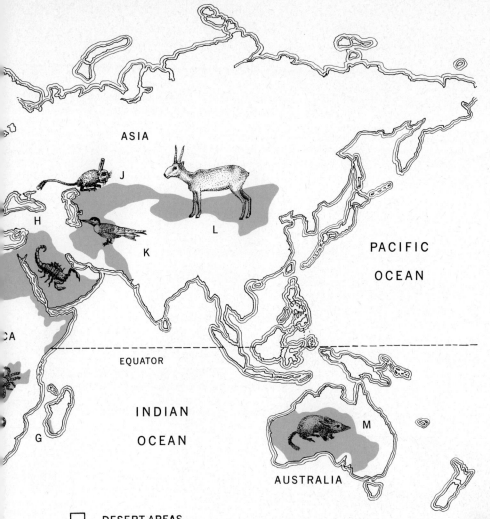

DESERT AREAS

A. NORTH AMERICAN   E. KALAHARI   J. TURKESTAN
B. ATACAMA   F. NAMIB   K. INDIAN
C. PATAGONIAN   G. MADAGASCAR   L. GOBI
D. SAHARA   H. ARABIAN   M. AUSTRALIAN

Man's misuse of the land also creates deserts, and in
North Africa and Arabia the natural deserts have been
increased in area by overgrazing, especially by sheep and
goats, traditional domesticated animals of these regions.

Cactus blossoms, in contrast to
the rest of the spiny plant, are
bright and beautiful. The leaves,
reduced to sharp spines, permit
practically no evaporation,
making the cactus ideally suited
to desert conditions.

1.35 inches a year, the mesquite is green. This shrub sends its roots
down as much as a hundred feet below the surface, to tap the underground streams fed by water coming down the sides of distant mountains.

Other desert plants make as much use of the sporadic rains as
possible. Instead of having deep roots like the mesquite, they have
roots which, although penetrating perhaps only a few inches, spread

(right)
Abrupt changes from barren land to luxuriant vegetation are rare; between extremes there are usually **areas of semiarid grassland** with varying amounts of vegetation. As one moves across these intermediate regions from the fertile areas towards the deserts, the vegetation becomes sparser and more like the cacti or tough, thorny bushes. Like the oases, semidesert areas help support a wide variety of animal life.

(above)
During much of the year the **boojum tree** has a **bare trunk,** which is used to store water. After the rains come, leaves appear for a few weeks and then drop off. Only the stems remain, as sharp thorns.

out over a large area. So they are able to draw on a large volume of soil for their water.

When water is scarce, precautions must be taken to see that it is shared out evenly. The creosote plant of the North American deserts does just this. It is an evergreen with shallow roots covering an extensive area. Like many other desert plants its roots give off substances called inhibitors, which prevent seeds falling near from germinating or the roots of nearby plants from growing too close. As a result creosote bushes are so evenly spaced that it looks as if they have been planted by someone who has measured out the ground. When a creosote bush dies, the next rain washes away the inhibitors from around its roots and the seeds that have been lying on the soil around it are now able to germinate. Each of these seedlings begins to secrete inhibitors from its roots and eventually only one survives to replace the old bush.

Although we generally think of plants taking in water only through the roots, some can take it in through the leaves. Certain desert plants obtain their water this way when there is no rain. Even in hot deserts there is sufficient water vapour in the air for dew to be formed during the cool of the night, and this dew is absorbed by some of the plants which are called dew-gluttons as a consequence. Some of them take in more water than they need and the excess is passed out through their roots to the benefit of other plants growing nearby.

Plants living in very dry situations, and known as xerophytes (Greek: *xeros*=dry, *phyton*=plant), have various ways by which the loss of water may be reduced. Typically, their leaves have few stomata, and these may be sunk in pits or protected by hairs to further reduce evaporation. More usually, the size of the leaf is reduced and its

(left)
The golden blooms of the **paloverde** adorn many desert landscapes in Mexico and the southwestern United States. In the spring, small leaves appear briefly. The tree manufactures its food through the chlorophyll in the bark of its bright green branches.

surface protected by a thick, waxy cuticle or, as in the creosote bush, by resin. There is another adaptation for reducing water loss. In this the proportion of surface area to volume is reduced. For example, the usual flat leaf has a very large surface area for its volume, and it will lose a large amount of water by evaporation; however, if the leaf is thicker, but with the same volume, its surface area will be less. Thus many desert plants have thick, rounded leaves. The best-known of these are the cacti, some of which consist of a single spherical body capable of storing a large amount of water, with leaves reduced to sharp spines that allow practically no loss by evaporation.

Other desert plants also store water in their tissues. These are called succulents because their tissues are soft and pulpy, holding a large volume of water. Cacti are the more familiar of these but there are others that lack the spines. In many succulents the stems are fluted, allowing for expansion of the inner tissues when they soak up water after it has rained. Other succulents, such as the yuccas and mesquites, store water below the ground in large fleshy taproots.

The types of plants discussed so far are called "drought resisters". By storing water or reducing the rate at which it is lost, they are able to carry on their life processes during times of drought. However, they will live very slowly, because not only is a flow of water necessary for taking up salts from the soil, but a large surface area is needed for the absorption of light for photosynthesis, the process by which food is manufactured. A plant that has only a small surface area of leaves will not be able to manufacture food very fast unless there is some subsidiary aid. Some desert plants overcome this difficulty by being able to carry out photosynthesis in the stems. The paloverde (Spanish for "green wood") grows tiny leaves in the spring. These are soon shed, but photosynthesis is carried on in the bark of the

(above)
The common American **agave,** the **century plant,** is very slow to mature. It has sharp-pointed fleshy leaves with spiny margins. It dies after producing a tall stem with clusters of flowers.

(left)
Desert **marigolds** are similar to the annual flowers in spring gardens. After a brief growing period, however, they liberate their seeds, which do not flower the following spring but only after the rains.

(above)
After a desert rainfall, **poppies** often appear in bright profusion. But their cheery sparkle lasts only a short period of time, for they flower, seed and die very quickly.

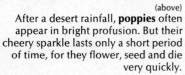

branches and twigs which are tinted green by chlorophyll, the pigment which absorbs light for photosynthesis.

Other desert plants are called "drought evaders". They evade the difficulties of carrying on life during drought conditions by ceasing to carry out their normal activities at such times. They lose their leaves, like the more familiar deciduous trees, but unlike these, the desert plants can drop their leaves at any time, perhaps two or three times a year. The creosote bush, at first sight, appears to be a drought evader because during a drought it throws off its green leaves, but instead of being completely bare, it is left with small brownish leaves. These are able to carry out sufficient photosynthesis, without much water loss, for the bush to survive considerable droughts, so it is actually a drought resister.

Some plants are able to survive drying up. The protoplasm, the substance of which all living things are made, is able to withstand desiccation. Numerous desert-living mosses and ferns, as well as higher plants, are able to survive due to having this quality. Some mosses are called resurrection plants and so are the fig marigold and the rose of Jericho. The latter lives in the deserts of Israel. It is a small woody plant which loses its leaves as the dry season comes on. The branches curl up, protecting the ripe seed pods. In this state it may get blown out of the loose sand and rolled about until it reaches a moist spot, or it may merely lie on the dry sand until the rains come again, when it takes root. The branches then unfurl and the seeds are released.

Usually in desert country only the succulent cacti and prickly pear and the thorny, withered-looking creosote bushes or desert hollies are to be seen. After a rainstorm, however, a lush vegetation springs up and bright flowers, such as primroses, poppies and marigolds, appear as it were suddenly from seeds lying dormant in the arid soil. The plants will throw out leaves, flower, seed and die, all in a short space of time.

These plants are very like the ordinary herbaceous annuals in our gardens which grow in spring, then die after a short growth period, liberating their seeds which will germinate in the following spring. A better name for these desert plants is ephemerals, that is plants that last for only a short time. Unlike our herbaceous plants they do not flower every spring, but only after the rains. Their success is based on the ability of their seeds to last for a long time, often many years, despite hot, dry conditions. For this reason the ephemerals are classified as "drought escapers".

Laboratory tests have shown the difference between the seeds of the drought escapers and the annual plants with which we are familiar. If the seeds of annuals are placed in dry soil which is then moistened, they will germinate, but those of the desert plants will not. Then, if the soil is allowed to dry out again and this time the

(left)
The relationship between the **yucca moth** and the **yucca plant** has been called a classic case of symbiosis. The moth cannot exist without the plant, on which it lives and lays its eggs; and the plant would not produce seeds without the moth, which carries pollen from flower to flower.

(below)
Yucca moth caterpillars feed on **yucca seeds,** but enough seeds mature to reproduce the plant.

(right)
The extreme form of desert is one that is made up of
sand dunes completely barren of vegetation, as in
North Africa. Here the **Arabian camel,** or **dromedary,**
has proved invaluable to the tribesmen, who must
move tents, flocks and children from oasis to oasis.

(center and far right)
Both the **Persian onager** (center right), and the **Asiatic
ass** (far right) are, like the camel, able to survive for
long periods of time without water.

seeds are watered from above to represent falling rain, they germinate.
The explanation is that the seed coats of the desert plants contain
inhibitors which prevent the seeds from germinating. Rain washing
over the seed coats gradually leaches out the inhibitors and allows
the seeds to germinate.

Delayed germination is very important to desert plants. If the seeds
were able to germinate as soon as moisture reached them they might
start to grow with only slightly moist conditions and then dry up
for lack of water. Even a layer of dew might initiate germination.
What is needed is that they should germinate in the rainy season when
there is likely to be enough water in the surface of the ground to allow
the ephemerals to grow and seed before it has evaporated or run off.

Large Desert Mammals

THE ONE ANIMAL traditionally associated with deserts is, of course,
the camel, because it has been inseparable from man's desert travels
since early times. Camels were brought west from Asia thousands of
years ago to be used in Asia Minor, then in North Africa. Since
then they have been imported to the deserts of North America and
Australia and into Spain, and in all three places they have gone
wild. Not only are they familiar animals, they have been intensively
studied in recent years to find out by what means they are able to
cope with desert conditions. This has contributed to our understanding
of the adaptations to desert life possessed by other animals.

(right)
Although many deserts are seemingly endless stretches
of shifting sands, others are bright with **vegetation**
and swarming with many kinds of **animal life,** each
variety of life specially suited to the harsh life of an
arid environment.

(above)
The **saiga antelope** of central Asia prefers wide treeless plains. Like so many other animals of the semidesert, it can go for long periods without drinking. The long, curving horns of the adult saiga have made it a popular target for hunters, who have brought it close to extinction.

(below)
This graceful, dainty **gazelle** inhabits the hot, rugged African and Arabian deserts. However, some species are extremely adaptable and can survive at high altitudes and in northern zoos.

A great deal of the early information written about camels has proved to be incorrect. Statements about the camel's ability to carry heavy loads over long distances at high speeds are exaggerated, as are claims about its water storage capacity. It has often been said that camels store water in their stomachs. This is based on reports of Arabs and other travellers, lost in the desert, being saved from dying of thirst by killing a camel and drinking the fluid in its stomach. The reports are correct, but the fluid in the stomach was not stored water but digestive juices, unpalatable to anyone but a dying man.

This is not to belittle the camel. It can stand up to hard conditions but no more so than several other animals. What we must do is to see the camel as it really is.

A camel can carry a load of over 200 pounds, but for the heavier loads it must be in first-class condition, the weather must be not too hot and the water holes frequent. Riding camels, as opposed to pack camels, have been known to travel ninety-five miles in thirteen hours. In Somaliland some camels travelled for six days without water. Camels have been put to greater trials than these but they have usually died in the process.

Although the camel's intake of water is prodigious, sometimes as much as twenty-seven gallons of water when the animal is thirsty, it is not so much this large volume of water in its body that enables it to survive in the desert; if dew-wetted vegetation or succulents are available the camel need not drink at all. Indeed, this is true for most desert animals. Where the camel scores over man in the matter of water supply is that it can survive a water loss equal to one-third of its body weight before it is in distress. A man dies after he has lost only one-sixth of his body weight.

Another winning feature of the camel's physiology is that during the heat of the day its body temperature can rise, from 93° F. in the morning to as much as 104° F. by midday. A man with a temperature of 104° F. would be critically ill. The advantage of being able to let the body temperature rise is that the animal does not have to use up its water supply in evaporation, by sweating or panting, to keep cool. Instead it is able to endure the heat and then cool off during the chill desert night.

The camel's hairy coat, also, helps not only to protect the body from excessive heat during the day, but to prevent a rapid cooling at night that would leave it too cold by morning. Other adaptations are the ability to eat dry thorny vegetation, long eyelashes and nostrils that can be closed to keep out wind-blown sand.

Another large desert-living animal that has also been domesticated by man is the ass. Like the camel it is able to survive long periods without water, and when water is plentiful it can drink as much as fifteen gallons at a time.

There are several different kinds of wild asses living in North Africa and south-west and central Asia. The different Asiatic asses are much alike but are given different names in different regions. In Mongolia they are called the kiang, kulan or chigetai, in Persia they are onager and in Pakistan ghorkar. The Nubian wild ass is still found between the Upper Nile, Ethiopia and the Red Sea, but like the asses in other parts it is hunted for its flesh and the foals are captured for domestication. In Algeria asses became extinct in Roman times, and there are no longer any asses in Syria or Arabia.

The question naturally arises why large animals of any kind should make their homes in deserts, where food and water are scarce and even small animals do not have an easy time. The answer is that very few animals belong exclusively to deserts. Because there are no hard and fast boundaries to a desert it is often hard to decide what animals are really living in the desert. Species that normally live where there is plenty of vegetation may move into the desert areas for a short time to feed on the sparse vegetation there, or they may migrate

Deer usually live in areas of abundant vegetation. The North American **mule deer** are no exception, although they sometimes stray around the fringes of the Arizona desert.

(right)
Because they both feed on carrion, **hyenas** and **vultures** can range widely throughout Africa; The dead bodies they eat are found in dry areas as well as in lush vegetation.

in during the rainy season when the ephemerals are growing. The red kangaroo of Australia is such an animal. It can live in a variety of conditions and so is widespread over the continent. It has become a pest because it competes for food and water with the sheep, and being able to make do with sparse dry vegetation can outgraze the sheep.

In North America the pronghorn antelope and the mule deer use deserts in the same way as the Australian kangaroo. Both species are found in nearly every kind of habitat, although the pronghorn is now fairly rare due to man's encroachment. An important feature in the habits of these animals is that outside the desert, where food is plentiful, they live together in large herds. When living in the desert they are more spaced out. There will be groups of a dozen or so animals, perhaps only two or three in very dry areas, instead of herds of hundreds. In desert areas, therefore, competition for food is not so great that the plants are completely eaten up, while the vegetation is not torn up nor the soil broken up by the stamping of hundreds of hoofs.

The deserts of the world form refuges from competition or persecution for many of those animals capable of standing up to them and this is notably true for various species of antelope. The Dorcas gazelle, one of the smallest and most graceful of the gazelles, lives in the dry areas of North Africa, while the Arabian gazelle is found in desert land farther east. In Asia there is the Mongolian gazelle or zeren on the dry steppes from Tibet to China, and the saiga and chiru live in central Asia, where vegetation is sparse and often the only water is in salty pools.

Unfortunately little is known of these desert antelopes: man has been too interested in killing them. The saiga was killed for its horns, which were powdered and used by the Chinese as a medicine, and the oryx of Africa and Arabia suffered because it is traditional that a piece of oryx hide around his rifle is an indication of an Arab's prowess as a hunter. Originally, exceptional skill was needed to

(opposite page)
Jack rabbits are actually hares, but with donkey ears like that, they quickly became the "jackasses of the rabbit world" to the early settlers of the West. The **black-tailed jack rabbit** shown here inhabits the dry, open areas of the American Southwest, while the range of the larger antelope jack rabbit is primarily in Mexico. Only in southern Arizona do their territories overlap. Both animals depend upon their speed for safety, being capable of leaping away from danger at 30 to 35 miles per hour.

track the wary oryx through the sandy plains of the desert. Now machine guns and motor cars have made the oryx a sitting target and it is only their ability to survive in the most remote parts of the deserts that has prevented the extinction of these antelopes.

Another antelope that is nearing the verge of extinction due to the attentions of hunters is the addax. This large antelope roams the Sahara desert and the surrounding lands. The long, spirally-twisted horns are the main attraction to hunters, but it is of interest more generally because of its ability to live in the driest parts of the desert. Its hoofs are short and widely splayed, enabling the addax to travel over the soft sands in rapid journeys in search of scanty food supplies. Indeed, its movements across the Sahara are linked with belts of rain encroaching on the desert from the Mediterranean or from the tropical forests to the south. It is said that the addax can determine where the rains have fallen, by scenting, from a distance, where the vegetation has turned green. At other times the addax, like the camel, is able to live on the coarsest vegetation. Mucus is secreted from the walls of the intestine to ease the passage of rough vegetation. It also serves to prevent the dry indigestible stalks from soaking up water before being evacuated, so robbing the addax of this essential substance.

Small Desert Mammals

THERE ARE NUMEROUS SMALL MAMMALS living in the deserts of the world. Because they are easier to handle than the large ones such as the oryx or gazelles, and because they do not move over such great distances, they have been studied in greater detail. It is not possible in a small space to deal with more than a few, and for this we will choose those that best illustrate adaptations to desert life, especially those that have been kept in laboratories and studied in great detail.

The chief species, in this respect, is undoubtedly the kangaroo rat, a small rodent living in the deserts of the south-western United States. The kangaroo rat is so called because it is a rat with long hind legs

(below, left)
In parts of the Near East **spiny mice** live in barren rocky areas or in sandy valleys. Often they occupy burrows made by gerbils, or find shelter in crevices or holes in the rocks. Dry seeds are their main food.

(below, center)
The semiarid, treeless Great Plains of North America are the home of numerous **prairie dogs.** These plump, short-eared rodents burrow in the ground and strip the land of vegetation.

(below, right)
Pack rats are found all over North America. Those living in deserts build their homes in cacti or in clumps of mesquite.

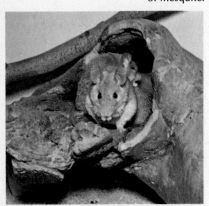

(left)
The **bannertail kangaroo rat** receives its name from the leaping motion it makes, similar to that of a kangaroo. Native to the deserts of the southwestern United States, this small rodent lives entirely on dry seeds and can live indefinitely without drinking.

that progresses in leaps, in the manner of a kangaroo. Long hind legs are a feature of many small desert animals. There are the jerboas of the Sahara, the jirds of Asia and the jerboa rats and marsupial jerboas of Australia. They all move by jumping, springing off with their hind legs using the long tail as a balancer, and they not only behave in the same way but tend to look alike. When this happens in several unrelated groups of animals it is called convergent evolution. This merely means that animals living under the same conditions come to resemble each other, although their ancestries may be very different. The long hind legs of small desert animals enable them to move rapidly over the loose, often shifting sand, in search of the scanty supplies of food. The kangaroo rat, only a few inches long, can leap six feet at a time so that it can collect sufficient food for the day, in the form of seeds scattered over a wide area, before the sun becomes too hot.

(above)
Collared peccaries are common in deserts as well as in forests. They move about in groups of five to fifteen, feeding mainly in the cooler hours of the day. Their apparently indestructible digestive systems make it possible for them to eat almost anything—from spiny cactus to snakes.

The kangaroo rat, or pocket-rat, has an advantage over other desert rodents in food-gathering. It has special pockets of skin on the outside of its cheeks. Anyone who has kept hamsters will be familiar with the way they collect their food and store it in pouches in the cheeks, to take it back to the nest. Kangaroo rats differ from hamsters in that the pouches open outside the mouth, but the principle is the same. The kangaroo rat crams seeds into the pouches, then empties them into its food store by stroking the pouches with its front paws.

Storing food against hard times is a common habit among rodents so it is not surprising to find it among the desert species also. After the rains the ephemerals and other plants quickly produce a crop of seeds. The rodents then lay up a store of these against times of scarcity.

This is not the only way of storing food. Some jerboas store their food inside their bodies, especially in the form of a thick layer of fat at the base of the tail.

The seeds that form the main items of diet of these animals are very dry, yet kangaroo rats have been found, under carefully controlled experiments, to be able to survive indefinitely without drinking.

More precise observations have shown that kangaroo rats, and other desert animals, have a number of remarkable adaptations for conserving the water that is already in their bodies. Perhaps the most important is that their urine is concentrated, containing just enough water to flush out the excess salts from the body. The feces are also very dry.

Another way water is lost from the body is in the breath. If you breathe on a cold window or mirror it clouds over, because the water vapour in your breath condenses on the glass. This represents a loss of water from the body. Kangaroo rats have special passages in their noses that cause the water vapour to condense from the breath before it leaves the body, the water then going back into circulation.

Despite these advantages the kangaroo rat is still bound to lose some water, so, if they are to exist without drinking, they must get water from somewhere to make good the loss. There will be a little in the seeds they eat, but this is only a very small percentage. The rest is obtained from what is known as physiological water. Carbohydrates in the seeds are broken down by the body chemistry and the hydrogen and oxygen elements in them combine to form water. We produce very little physiological water and the amount is very small compared to the amount that passes through the body, but in desert rodents, in which water loss in the breath, urine and feces is reduced to a minimum, only a relatively small amount of physiological water is sufficient to replace it.

Adopting special habits to escape from the worst of the desert conditions also helps an animal to survive on little or no water. Small desert mammals are usually nocturnal or at most are out and about in early morning or late evening, so they are never exposed to the fierce heat of the sun. During the day they lie up in burrows. Al-

The **ring-tail cat** (left side of photograph), also called the coon cat or cat-squirrel, lives on rodents, lizards and sometimes birds. The **coati**, or **coatimundi** (right side), feeds on insects, lizards, fruit and birds' eggs. Both are native to Central and South America, but the ring-tail cat is also found in the southern United States and the coatimundi has recently extended its range northwards into Arizona.

though the sand on the surface may be scorching hot, a few inches down it is cool and moist. Studies of the jerboa in Egypt showed that on days when the temperature of the surface sand went up to 104° F. the temperature in the burrow never went above 79° F. Furthermore the humidity of the air in the burrow was from two to five times greater than that of the outside air. The jerboas were able to adjust conditions within the burrow by changing the depth to which it was dug. The farther they go down the lower is the temperature, and it is constant by day and by night. In the hot summer months, also, they seal up the entrance of the burrow with sand to keep the hot daytime air out.

So far we have only discussed the two small desert mammals the scientists know best. Although it is impossible to mention them all here, we can meet some of the others. Like the large desert mammals, some of the small mammals do not really belong to the desert. A French zoologist working in a part of the Sahara made a count of all the kinds of mammals living there. Of the fifty-eight he found, only twenty-eight were true desert species, that is, animals specially adapted for living in dry conditions. The others had, so to speak, wandered in temporarily from the surrounding semi-dry areas for what they could pick up.

We have already noted that all the desert mammals tend to have the same adaptations such as the long hind legs and nocturnal and burrowing habits. Their hue also is much the same, being sandy or some shade near it. It is often said that this is a protective coloration, concealing the animals from their enemies. Whether this is so or not is still a matter of opinion. One may argue that rodents coming out only at night have little need of camouflage. Against this the supporters of the protective coloration theory retort that in deserts the moon and also the stars are so bright that the landscape is bathed with silvery light and that camouflage is still necessary even at night. However, there

(above, left)
By changing the depth of the tunnels in which it lives, the **African jerboa** maintains an ingenious climate control. The farther down it goes, the lower the temperature becomes. During the summer it insulates the burrow against the hot air by sealing the entrance with sand.

(above, right)
The **Russian jerboa,** like its relatives in Africa, moves by springing off its hind legs; its tail is used to maintain balance.

(above, left)
The **Cape jumping hare,** like many other desert rodents, has long hind legs and burrowing habits. It is not really a hare but something like a large jerboa.

(above, right)
The **desert cougar,** or mountain lion, tends to be slimmer and lighter than the forest species. It hunts at night and remains hidden during the day.

is the disturbing fact that the few species of bats inhabiting the Sahara are also light in hue, and they do not have to merge into a background of sand for protection.

So far we have met only the animals which eat seeds, vegetation, insects and such things. In any community there are also the flesh-eaters that keep the numbers of the vegetable and insect feeders in check. In North America there are no special desert flesh-eaters. The same beasts of prey that hunt in the surrounding country come into the desert at times to feed. These include the puma or cougar and the bobcat, a kind of lynx. In Australia there is the native cat or dasyure that is to be found all over the continent, and the crest-tailed marsupial mouse. This killer of rats and mice has the habit of eating its prey from head to tail, turning the skin back as it goes and leaving the empty skin inside out. It also basks in the sun, an unusual habit for desert-living animals.

In the Sahara desert the fennec foxes, dainty little animals half the size of the common red fox, live in burrows in the same way as the rodents. They have hairy soles on their feet so that they can run easily on sand. Fennec foxes have characteristically enormous ears. Like the big ears of the jerboas, these are supposed to act as radiators, providing a large surface area from which excess body heat can be lost. However, they not only have large external ears but the inner ear, the internal hearing mechanism, is also well developed, for predatory animals, like the vegetarians they feed on, have a scattered food supply and they must always be on the alert to detect the movements of their prey from a distance.

Sometimes, however, the vegetarians live in colonies, like the stick-nest rats of Australia. Several rats work together building a communal nest of twigs. Remarkably, they put stones on top to prevent the nests from blowing away. More often desert rodents are solitary. Another French scientist working in the Sahara counted only one desert rat in one square mile, and took six months to find a fat-tailed gerbil.

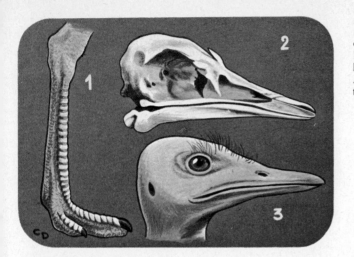

(left)
Like the camel, the **ostrich** has **long lashes of hairlike feathers** (3) which are helpful in keeping sand out of its eyes. Its **long legs** and **large feet** (1) are well suited to desert travel. Also pictured here is the bone structure of the skull (2).

(below)
A small bird living in the desert areas of Mexico and the southwestern United States, the **elf owl** nests in cavities in the giant saguaro cactus. When hungry, it catches insects on the wing.

Birds and Reptiles

VERY FEW BIRDS are true desert dwellers. Like some of the mammals certain kinds will penetrate into the desert if food becomes available there. We have seen that speed of movement is of advantage to desert dwellers in enabling them to cover large areas in search of food, and, of course, birds are particularly well off in this respect. If, for example, an oryx or wild ass dies, its bones will soon be picked clean by vultures. As the air above the sand is warmed it rises in thermals. Vultures use these thermals to soar to great heights so that they can spot a carcass from many miles away.

Several birds of prey breed along the fringes of the desert, where they can find nesting places in which their young can be protected from the sun. The elf owl, of Mexico and southern United States, is one of the smallest of owls, the size of a house sparrow. Elf owls live on insects and on occasional small rodents such as the kangaroo rat. They often nest in the giant saguaro cacti using holes excavated by the Gila (pronounced *heela*) woodpeckers. The woodpeckers dig holes to find the insects they feed on and also to make nesting cavities. The nest holes have a tough lining of hardened sap and are later used by flycatchers and sparrow hawks, as well as by woodpeckers. The California quail also lives in the semi-desert areas of Mexico and the United States. Where there is succulent vegetation for it to eat, it can go for months or years without water.

For truly desert birds we can turn to the most familiar, the ostrich. Photographs of ostriches usually show trees and buildings in the background because nowadays most ostriches are to be found on farms where they are reared for their billowing white feathers. Nevertheless, ostriches have several features by which they qualify as inhabitants of deserts. Their eyelids have long lashes that are made up of fringes of hairlike feathers. In fact, to look at, the eyes of an ostrich and a camel are strikingly similar. The long legs and large feet of this

(above)
Chachalacas, named for their call, inhabit the warmer, drier parts of tropical America. They belong to the same family as pheasants and barnyard fowls.

(above)
Different birds use different methods to take their young from nest to ground. The **chachalaca** not only carries them down, clinging to her legs, but also carries them back up again to roost for the night.

(above)
Like other vultures, the **turkey vulture** feeds on carrion. A powerful flier, it can range far across deserts, finding carrion by sight and possibly through its sense of smell.

flightless bird give it the ability to run very fast, another feature of desert animals. As with other birds, an ostrich has no external **ear,** but there is the usual tube leading to the eardrum. These tubes could easily become filled with windblown sand, but the ostrich can close its ears. This is something that can be readily seen in a zoo, where it is possible to view the bird at close quarters. The reflex of shutting and opening the ear periodically persists even when the need for it is no longer present.

It is often said that ostriches leave their eggs exposed in the sand for the heat of the sun to incubate them, but if they did this the eggs would be parboiled. In fact, the hen ostrich incubates them continuously throughout the day, while the male takes over from her at night..

Another truly desert bird, also in Africa, is the sand grouse. It lives on seeds and green shoots, when these are available, and this bird is unusual in that the adults bring water back to the nest stored in their crops. Back at the nest they bring the water up into the beak for the nestlings to drink. The cock also brings water to the hen in this way while she is incubating. This habit, at first sight rather strange, is only an extension of the behaviour of other birds, such as gulls, in which the male brings food back to the incubating hen.

In the Kalahari desert of south-west Africa there are several kinds of desert larks, but not much is known of their habits. A near relative in north-east Africa, the hoopoe-lark, uses its long curved bill to probe the sand for locust grubs.

The next group of animals we have to deal with are the reptiles. Those living in deserts are mainly snakes and lizards which are apparently successful desert dwellers, as many kinds of snakes and lizards are to be found living in deserts throughout the world. Their problems are the same as for other groups of animals but there is an additional one. Mammals and birds are warm-blooded. This means that their internal chemistry regulates their temperature, keeping them warm in cold conditions and cool in hot conditions, although the system breaks down in the most extreme conditions. However, cold-blooded animals, such as reptiles, cannot regulate their body temperature in this way. Consequently, it fluctuates with the temperature of the surrounding air. This means that a desert reptile becomes very cold at night. Then, as the sun rises it starts to thaw out, eventually becoming active and starting to feed, running around in search of prey. Later in the day, as the sun grows stronger, these same reptiles are in danger of heat-stroke and have to seek the shade.

Reptiles are, however, able to control their body temperatures to some extent by their behavior. Burrowing in the sand, where at a few inches' depth the temperature is constant, enables them to keep warm at night and cool during the day. Then, when they come to the surface in the morning, by lying sideways to the sun their flanks can absorb solar radiation to warm the body. Later in the day they lie head on to the sun so that less of the body surface is presented to the solar rays and they can avoid the worst effects of the heat.

Like other desert animals, lizards have adaptations for life on sand. They often have flaps or fringes on their toes which serve the same purpose as the hairy soles of the fennec, allowing them to get a firm grip on the sand. The desert agama of Africa moves about quickly not only to seek food and avoid enemies but to find shelter from the sun. The basilisk of Central America can run on its hind legs and, in more fertile habitats, it can even cross rivers, running, or scuttering, over the surface of the water.

On the other hand, the skinks, known as sandfish, "swim" through the sand. The toes are fringed with scales and act as paddles pushing

Called a "toad" because of its squat body, the **horned toad** is really a lizard that lives in the deserts of the southwestern United States, where it feeds on insects. It burrows into the sand with only its head showing and sweeps in passing ants with its tongue.

the lizards forward. One kind of skink living in the deserts of Pakistan has tiny limbs, useless for paddling. All the propulsion comes from side-to-side movements of the body and tail, so that it moves through sand much as a fish swims through water.

Swimming through sand means that more protection is needed against loose sand grains. Protecting the eyes some lizards have hoods of skin forming lids, sometimes with a fringe of enlarged scales like eyelashes along the free edges. Other lizards have special transparent scales covering the eye that act as goggles. The eardrum is also covered by protective scales, and a few lizards have muscular valves that allow the nostrils to be closed.

Many lizards burrow in the sand, to escape the sun, their enemies or as a means of lying in wait for their prey. The horned lizard, or horned toad as it is more usually called, that lives in Mexico and southern United States feeds on ants. It digs itself into the sand and lies in wait with only its head showing. Any ants that wander near it are captured by the horned toad with its tongue. The chuckwalla, on the other hand, which lives in the same region, takes refuge in crevices in rocks. If any predator tries to dislodge it, the chuckwalla blows up its body so that it is jammed tightly in the crevice.

The spring-tailed agama of North Africa and western Asia rushes into its burrow when disturbed. It then sticks its spiny tail out of the entrance, and whips it from side to side to deter the enemy. If it hears an enemy approaching while it is in its burrow it runs to the entrance and blocks it with its tail. The local peoples of the Asian deserts take advantage of this, brushing the ground with thorny branches to imitate a snake's rustles. The agama puts its tail out and is seized, for the tail is regarded as a delicacy.

The other main group of desert reptiles are the snakes, puff adders, various species of vipers and rattlesnakes. These, also, avoid the intense heat by burrowing or lying up in crevices and have devices to protect

(below, left)
The **Central American basilisk** can run on its hind legs. It lives in trees but **can cross rivers,** scuttling over the surface of the water. The male is crested from head to tail.

(below, right)
Australia's **moloch lizard** is a fearsome sight. It is grotesquely patterned in orange and brown, and it is covered with spine-tipped cones. But it is actually quite inoffensive, chiefly concerned with its usual meal of 1,000 or more ants.

them from sand grains. Most desert snakes have a ridge over the eye to keep sand out and some have nostrils that can be closed. Snakes have no ears to protect, they can only "feel" vibrations through the ground.

Snakes moving over the desert sand leave a peculiar trail, in the form of short straight tracks in parallel series. This is due to the special method of moving over a surface where the snake's body cannot get a good grip. If an ordinary snake is put on a sheet of glass it has difficulty moving in the normal manner, so it throws coils of its body forwards. In effect, it is working like a caterpillar tractor. A part of each coil is always in contact with the ground. As the snake moves, another part of the body is laid down on the ground in front of the part already there, which is then picked up. The body thus moves sideways like a coiled spring. Snakes that move like this in the deserts, such as a viper living in North Africa and Arabia and a rattlesnake in the United States, are called sidewinders.

On the ground, **whipsnakes** move sideways like coiled springs. Because they can move among the branches of bushes as easily as they can over ground, they are extremely difficult to catch among rocks and shrubs.

Insects and Other Small Animals

S O FAR, THE ANIMALS we have met have all been vertebrates, or animals with backbones. In the deserts there are many kinds of invertebrates, or animals without backbones, such as insects, scorpions,

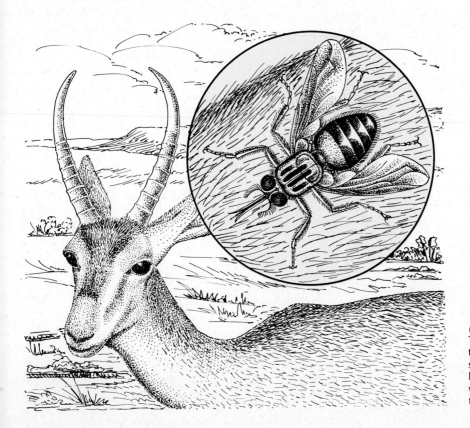

(left)
This seemingly insignificant fly is the **tsetse fly,** the transmitter of sleeping sickness to man. In addition, whole herds of domestic animals have been wiped out by the disease carried by this insect.

Related to the locust, the traditional plague of the desert regions of Africa, the **short-winged grasshopper,** or lubber, moves about in search of water supplies. It is found in the American southwest.

spiders and snails. The best-known desert insects are the locusts, which are renowned for the way in which they invade the countryside in swarms, stripping the vegetation so completely that they will turn land into a temporary desert. Yet they are not really desert dwellers; they are one of the many kinds of animals that live on the fringes of the desert and penetrate into it when conditions become favourable.

Locusts need water at all stages of their lives. The eggs have to take up water before they can develop and the young locusts need fresh green shoots for food. Like the human nomads, Bedouin Arabs for instance, locusts move around in search of water supplies. When there has been a rainstorm in a part of the desert and the plants shoot up, the locusts move in to feed and lay their eggs.

All invertebrate animals are cold-blooded, so they have the same problems as the reptiles already discussed. They cannot regulate their body temperature, so are in danger of overheating in the desert sun. Although insects have hard impermeable skins, they still lose a large amount of water by evaporation in hot weather. There is an advantage in being a larger insect because the larger its body the more water it can lose before drying up, so other things being equal the bigger insects have a better chance of survival in hot places.

Small insects have another advantage, however, in being able to utilize the smallest areas of shade, in shadows thrown by a tuft of grass or a pebble. Long-bodied insects use the trick used by the desert reptiles. When the sun is low they turn their bodies at right angles to it to make the most of its rays, and during the heat of the day they stand facing the sun, exposing as little body surface as possible. Locusts avoid the extreme cold of the desert night by climbing into the bushes and trees in evening, because it is the layer of air nearest the ground that cools most rapidly. In the morning the locusts return to the ground as the surface heats up again.

More properly belonging to the desert are the beetles, mostly the wingless tenebrionid beetles. These beetles can live in some of the driest parts of the desert. Most of them have rounded bodies which will absorb less heat than a flat or irregularly shaped body because they have a smaller surface area in proportion to size. Many of the beetles are shiny, reflecting back the sun's rays so that less heat enters their bodies, and they also have thick skins to help keep the heat out. Furthermore, some desert beetles have a layer of air trapped between the body and wing cases, which helps insulate the body, in the same way as Arabs wear loose-fitting clothes that trap an insulating layer of air.

Beetles living in the sandy parts of the deserts have flattened limbs, often with fringes of bristles. These help them to move over the sand, and to burrow into it, for they spend the heat of the day under the sand, only coming out at night. Other beetles live in rocky regions and have very long legs, on which they scuttle about, seeking

(above, left)
The large hairy spiders, popularly
called **tarantulas,** capture their prey by
sheer force. They are strong enough
to overpower small lizards and rodents.

(above, right)
Night hunters, **scorpions** stay hidden
all day, looking for insects after
twilight. Their sting comes from the
last joint of the tail. Although it is
often said that they never drink, many
scientists believe that they lick up dew.

both shade and food. Their long legs also lift their bodies above the very hot layer of air next to the sand.

Another important desert insect is a termite or white ant. This insect can survive in the deserts because it lives in colonies of hundreds of thousands. An individual termite would not survive long in the hot, dry desert air, but a termite colony is so organized that none of its members comes into contact with the outside atmosphere.

The colony lives in a nest, called a termitarium, which has solid walls built of sand or earth cemented together with saliva from the termites' mouths. These walls are so hard they can only be broken with a pickaxe, and, needless to say, they provide insulation from the sun's heat. Within the nest the air is kept relatively cool and humid by a system of air conditioning. The termites' method of obtaining water for the air conditioning is truly remarkable. They burrow down to the layer of water trapped beneath the desert, perhaps a hundred feet down. A continual procession of termites passes up and down the walls of these vertical shafts. When they reach the bottom they fill their crops with water and carry it back to the nest.

Termites feed on wood, or anything made of wood, such as paper. Some of them manage to live in parts of the Sahara where there is no vegetation at all, and it was something of a mystery how they managed to do this. It seems that they live on the remains of trees that grew there before the Sahara became a desert and which are now buried beneath the sand.

When attacking a piece of wood, the termites tunnel into it and eat it away leaving just a thin outer shell which protects the termites from the outside air. It is this habit that makes termites such a pest in the tropics. They attack the wooden parts of buildings, but the damage is not detected until the wood just crumbles away when touched.

There are also many different kinds of real ants living in deserts. Many of these are not desert animals, but are just taking advantage of any moisture or scrap of vegetation, which is hoarded to tide the ant colony over a dry period. The leaf-cutting ants of the South American deserts take pieces of leaf back to their nest where they chew them up.

A kind of fungus grows on the chewed-up leaves and is eaten by the ants when other supplies of food are low. Other ants store seeds in tunnels waterproofed by sand and saliva cement so that they do not germinate when it rains.

Perhaps the most extraordinary form of food storage is seen in the honey ants of the deserts of Australia, South Africa and North America. Some of the ants act as living containers. After a fall of rain foraging ants come back to the nest with their crops full of honey dew given off by scale insects living on the plants that have sprung up, or of nectar from the flowers. They then empty the sweet juices into the mouths of special individuals, known as repletes, that hang upside-down from the ceilings of the tunnels. The repletes do not digest the sap, they store it. As more and more is fed to them their abdomens swell up to the size of peas. Later, when food is scarce, they allow the juices to trickle from their mouths and the other ants lap it up.

Related to the insects are the spiders and scorpions, which are also invertebrates with hard bodies, but with four pairs of legs instead of three possessed by insects. Both are to be found in deserts, hiding under stones or in burrows in the sand. They usually lie up during the day and come out at night to hunt, for all spiders and scorpions are carnivorous. In fact, scorpions often eat spiders, and they both hunt insects, catching them, then quickly killing them with a special poison. The scorpions' poison comes from a sting in the last joint of the tail and that of spiders is injected through hollow fangs. To a great extent they get all the moisture they need from the juices of their prey, but they probably lick up dew as well.

Another group of invertebrate animals to be found in deserts are snails. With soft, fleshy bodies they seem hardly suited to live anywhere but in moist conditions. Yet in bad weather they retreat into their shells, sealing the entrance with a layer of cement. Even in temperate regions snails will do this to avoid very hot or very cold weather, so it is not surprising to find that some species are able to live in the deserts, burrowing down into the sand and sealing themselves into their shells when conditions become too hot and dry, and coming out to feed after rainstorms have brought out the ephemeral plants.

Sealed in their shells they can survive for long periods. This is illustrated by the story of a naturalist who collected some snail shells from a desert and presented them to the Natural History Museum in London. They were gummed to a board and put in a showcase. Years later they were found crawling around. They were able to survive for such a long time because they can store a large amount of fluid in their bodies, gathered in the form of dew. However, to put it in this way is an oversimplification, and it is not easy to explain why the snails eventually came out. It is sufficient for our purpose to record, and enjoy, this well-known, but always amusing, story.

Brine shrimp thrive in salty water. They swarm in large numbers and feed on microscopic, salt-tolerant plants. Common to the waters of the Great Salt Lake in Utah, they can also be found in many brine pools.

ARCTIC-ALPINE

HUDSONIAN ZONE
9,000 FEET

CANADIAN ZONE
7,000 FEET

TRANSITION ZONE
5,500 FEET

UPPER SONORAN
4,500 FEET

LOWER
SONORAN
3,500 FEET

Just as the climate is different **at varying elevations, the wildlife community changes** radically but predictably as well. The same ecological niche may be occupied by six different species of flycatchers, for instance, each at a different altitude.

Life in Cold Deserts

ALL THE ANIMALS AND PLANTS so far discussed live in hot deserts, but a considerable part of the land surface of the earth is cold desert. As we have seen, although the polar regions are covered in water in the form of ice and snow, they are true deserts because if we convert the snow that falls in one year into the equivalent amount of rain, it would amount to the same sort of volume as the annual rainfall of a hot desert. Furthermore, as the water is solid it cannot be used by plants and animals, except by the large animals like penguins which take mouthfuls of snow to quench their thirst.

The depths of the polar regions are, indeed, as barren as the depths of the Sahara desert, but even so we find animals that are able to spread into these inhospitable regions. American scientists living at the South Pole have reported seeing a skua flying overhead. A skua is a sea bird, cousin to the gulls, and lives on fish and any scraps or carrion it can find. Why it should have penetrated so far into the Antarctic continent no one knows.

Of more importance is the discovery by a party of British scientists of a colony of another kind of sea bird, the snow petrel. This is a dove-sized bird with pure white plumage and jet-black beak, eyes and feet. Snow petrels spend most of the year out at sea feeding on the small shrimplike animals that live near the surface. Every spring they return to the land to nest in crevices on cliff faces. It was on such a cliff, in a mountain range two hundred miles inland, that the explorers found this colony of snow petrels. It seemed very extraordinary that the birds should nest so far from the sea because they have to fly enormous distances to collect food for their young.

This discovery illustrates the essential feature of most of the life in the polar regions. Around the fringes of the Antarctic continent, or around the northern coasts of Canada or Siberia, there is teeming life. To all intents these ice-bound regions are not deserts at all. In the Antarctic there are vast colonies of penguins, some colonies containing several hundred thousand individuals. There are also other sea birds, like the skuas and snow petrels, as well as different kinds of seals. In the Arctic there are also sea birds and seals, walruses and polar bears. But these animals are not permanent inhabitants. Like some of the animals in the hot deserts, they are not really desert animals. For penguins, seals and the like their proper home is in the sea, which in the polar regions is teeming with small life, small sea creatures, that make up their food. The seals and sea birds go on land only to breed or to sleep.

On the landward side of the North Polar regions there are large

(below, left)
Most at home in the sea, **seals** go on land for breeding or sleeping only. In the polar regions the sea is full of food, which these animals sometimes obtain by diving down more than 400 feet.

(below, right)
The **polar bear** is insulated from the cold by its long shaggy coat, which, by trapping a layer of air, prevents body heat from escaping. Hairy soles on its feet help in crossing the ice.

land animals that spread into the cold deserts. Musk-ox and caribou in Canada and reindeer in Europe and Asia feed on the abundant summer vegetation, then survive the winter by digging up mosses and lichens from under the snow. Smaller animals also follow these habits, or hibernate, and flesh-eaters like wolves and Arctic foxes eke out the winter by killing the small animals during the summer, storing their carcases among the rocks, and returning to them in winter.

Looking more closely at the polar animals we find they have some of the features of the hot desert animals. Their coats are long and shaggy, trapping a layer of air that prevents the body's heat from being lost, whereas the hot desert animals, such as camels, have long coats to keep hot air away from their bodies. Polar bears have hairy soles to their feet to assist in walking over ice, just as the fennec has for walking over loose sand. Camels and the addax have splayed feet for walking on sand, while caribou and reindeer have similar hoofs for walking on ice. When they walk over hard ground the two halves of each hoof can be heard clicking together, like castanets, as the foot is lifted.

The differences lie in the shape of the body. Fennec foxes and jerboas of the Sahara have large ears that act as radiators and help the body lose surplus heat. The polar animals, like the Arctic fox, have comparatively small ears, preventing the loss of precious heat. This feature is shown most strikingly in North America. In the southern United States the hares, known as jack rabbits, have long ears. As we go north, and the climate gets colder, the various kinds of hare have progressively shorter ears until we come to the Arctic hare of northern Canada which has the shortest ears of all.

Leaving aside these animals that live on the fringes of the cold deserts, there is some real desert life in the polar regions. Parties of men travelling over the snowy wastes of the Antarctic have come across patches of green, yellow or red snow. These patches are tinted by

(above)
The **continent of Antarctica** contains the world's **largest cold desert,** with water frozen in many shapes and forms. However, only a few animals, such as the penguin, are able to take advantage of all this water for drinking purposes.

Walking across the ice, the **reindeer** is aided by its **splayed feet.** As each foot is lifted, a slipping tendon causes its two halves to click together.

minute, single-celled plants. Even when the temperature is many degrees below zero, the sun causes a slight melting of the snow and this provides sufficient water for the plants. Normally they are distributed very thinly over the surface of the snow, but where the snow melting (called ablation) is more intense the plants are swept together in patches.

There is more life, also, on the patches of rock, on cliff faces or flat areas where the snow melts away in summer. Here lichens become established, collecting water from snow that melts as the rocks warm up in the sun. In some places mosses can grow and where there are streams of meltwater small patches of grass can grow. In among the mosses and grass the air is humid and certain small invertebrates are to be found living on fungi and dead organic matter. These include mites, relatives of the spiders and scorpions of the hot deserts, wingless flies, primitive insects known as springtails and various kinds of worms. These are very lowly kinds of life and they are able to survive in the extremely cold conditions of the polar winter either as eggs or because the adults are able to go into a state of suspended animation in which the tissues will not be harmed by the cold.

There are other cold deserts that are not covered by ice and snow. One of these is the Gobi desert in Mongolia. Although it is at the same latitude as France it is much colder, being situated on a high plateau. During the short two-month summer it becomes carpeted with long grass, and nomadic tribes move in with their yaks and camels. For the rest of the year the Gobi is arid and swept by fierce, freezing winds, and except for stretches along the rivers flowing through it, the desert does not look very different from the Sahara.

The Gobi desert is so remote and inaccessible that we in the West know little about the wildlife there. However, recently there has come news that brings our story of desert animals to a complete circle. For many years there have been reports of camels that had gone feral, that

(below, left)
For the people who live at high altitudes in Central Asia, the **yak** is an important asset. It is a source of transportation, food and shelter.

(below, right)
Much of Central Asia is desert or semidesert. There the two-humped, **Bactrian camel** plays the same role that its one-humped relative, the Arabian camel, plays in southwestern Asia and northern Africa.

is, domesticated Bactrian camels that had gone wild. This would not be surprising as there are feral Arabian camels in California, Spain and Australia.

Recently Mongolian zoologists have been able to confirm that these are truly wild camels living in the desert. They have been able to catch one and keep it in a zoo and films have been taken of others. The camels they found had two humps, like the domestic Bactrian camels that are used in Asia, and it is thought that these wild camels are the last wild descendants of the stock from which all the domestic camels in Africa and Asia are descended.

The zoologists were able to show that these wild camels are different from the domesticated camels in several ways. Their legs are more slender and their feet are smaller. The coat is thinner, there is no mane, and the ears are shorter. These wild camels were difficult to find not only because of their rarity and wariness but because they are nomadic, being continually on the move in small groups, making their way around the desert in search of the scanty vegetation.

On long journeys across desert sands, the camel's remarkable ability to survive for many days without water and to withstand the extreme changes in temperature from day to night has given it the name of **"ship of the desert."**

► *Colorful and hardy plants that can make even the desert bloom.*

Wild Flowers of the Desert

THE DESERT IS A CHALLENGE—to the plants, to the animals and to man. And of all living things, man is distinguished by his love of a challenge. So it is that the desert has long fascinated and will continue to fascinate mankind. The desert presents clear-cut and stringent living conditions to the plants and animals that make it their home. Either they live successfully with these conditions or they die—there is no alternative. Because the desert plants and animals have accepted this challenge and have been successful, they excite our interest and admiration. Especially is this true when the desert plants, having survived the hazards of the desert climate, flaunt their success with a frivolous display of attractive flowers, the promise of another generation of the species to follow.

What Is a Desert?

DESERTS ARE AREAS characterized by low rainfall and high temperatures. These two basic factors operate to produce other characteristics of the desert, such as a high rate of evaporation, wide daily range of temperature, light of great intensity, low humus content and high salt content of the soil, and erosion by wind and water.

Factors That Shape the Desert

A WARM LAND AREA which receives less than ten inches of rainfall a year is generally considered to be a desert. In addition to its scarcity, rainfall is often erratically distributed over an area and unevenly

In the desert, water often determines what will live and what will die—whether it be man, beast or plant. For plants, water also determines, to a great extent, their appearance and their life span. To retain life-giving moisture, a variety of adaptations appear among plants. For example, because it is of such great importance to retain water and not allow it to evaporate, a plant's leaves may be thick and have bristly or waxy coverings, or they may be small, with a shorter distance between the leaf and the source of the moisture. In the photograph at the top right, **Perky Sue blossoms** enliven the desert landscape of the American Southwest. As a moisture-retaining aid, its leaves are hairy and often rather sparse.

MEL HUNTER

distributed throughout the year. There are some desert areas which have undergone periods of no rainfall of several years duration, and others which have received their yearly average or double their yearly average in a single storm. In some deserts there is one season during which rain normally falls; in others rainfall is divided between two seasons.

The lack of moisture limits the number and types of plants that can grow in a desert. Yet sudden storms sometimes occur, and the downrush of water then has a dramatic effect, eroding and moving the substance of the desert soil, which is only partially protected and held in place by the scarce plant growth.

High daytime temperatures during at least part of the year are a desert characteristic. The highest official temperature recorded on earth was 136.4° F. in the shade in the Sahara. An official temperature of 134° F. was recorded in Death Valley, in the United States.

A wide daily variation in the temperature and a wide seasonal temperature variation are also common in deserts. Moisture in the air acts as an insulating blanket that absorbs a great deal of the sun's rays in humid regions, and also prevents heat from being rapidly lost by re-radiation into space after sunset. In the desert, however, humidity is usually so slight that the air is a relatively inefficient insulator. Solar heat reaches the ground easily during the day in the desert and, in turn, this heat is largely lost by radiation, unimpeded by moisture in the air at night. The result is a wide variation between the daytime and nighttime temperatures and rapid temperature changes soon after sunrise and sunset. Differences in daily temperature ranges of fifty to sixty degrees are frequently recorded in some desert areas. Lack of humidity and cloud cover in the desert also produces a high percentage of sunny days with light of great intensity.

High temperatures produce a high rate of evaporation of the scanty moisture available in the desert. The strong winds which are common in desert areas not only contribute to the evaporation rate—they largely account for the typical appearance of a desert landscape; the abundance of plant life whose roots help to "bind" the soil, and whose upper parts break the force of the wind just above ground level are absent. As a result the winds sweep across the unprotected earth, eroding it continuously. The earth is ever on the move, often as shifting dunes; and its substance, borne on the winds, acts as an abrasive that relentlessly re-sculptures the exposed rocks.

Desert Soils Tend to Be Highly Mineralized

THE CONTINUOUS WEATHERING OF THE ROCKS of the desert produces a soil with a high mineral content. In moister climates the soil minerals are likely to be carried deep below the surface by water soaking through it. Not so in the desert, where rainfall sufficiently plentiful to penetrate the soil to any great depth is rare. As a result,

The bright flowers of the **lupine** plant can be seen blooming in many arid regions. Their leaves radiate from a central point, and so they are said to be palmately divided (like the palm of a hand).

(left)
The low-growing **sand verbenas** with their trailing stems provide bright spots of color early in the spring. Some species bloom a second time in September, for the plants seem to have some **resistance to the summer heat,** staying green for a long time.

desert soils are often superior in mineral content and would be capable of producing a plentiful plant life if they could be supplied with water. In other cases, however, the minerals may be so excessive, or such undesirable ones as far as most plants are concerned, that vegetation is either absent or consists only of certain highly specialized types of plants.

Desert soils are lacking in humus. With only a limited plant cover to live, die and decompose on the desert soil, the humus content is understandably low.

(above)
A familiar sight in the Chihuahuan Desert of Mexico. Texas and New Mexico (where they have been named the state flower), **yuccas** produce huge masses of creamy white or greenish white bell-shaped blossoms. They are pollinated solely by small, white female yucca moths, which carry the pollen from one flower to another.

Where Are the World's Deserts?

ONE-SEVENTH OF THE EARTH'S LAND SURFACE is covered by deserts. These arid areas are found in the Northern and the Southern hemispheres and fall generally between the latitudes of 15° and 40°, forming a pair of irregular and much broken "belts". Thus there are deserts in south-western North America, in two locations in South America, in southern Africa, over much of Australia, and as a belt of desert land that stretches intermittently from northern Africa across the Arabian Peninsula and on across portions of the Asian continent.

These deserts are caused primarily by lack of moisture. The winds passing over them are mostly dry—usually as a result of having had their water content condensed out in passing over high mountains. Even the monsoon winds from the Indian Ocean that bring torrential rains for weeks at a time to Burma, Malaysia and eastern India are "dried out" by the time they reach deep into the Asian mainland.

This condition is caused by the pattern of air movement over the earth's surface. Due to the rotation of the earth and related factors this pattern of air movement, in general, consists of descending air over the two desert "belts" along the Tropic of Cancer and the Tropic of Capricorn. This air is warmed in its descent and warm air being capable of holding more moisture than cool air, it picks up additional moisture, rather than releasing any it may already be carrying.

The Sahara is the largest of the world's deserts, stretching completely across North Africa and covering over 3,000,000 square miles of land. This enormous area is characterized by barren rocks, sand and extremely sparse vegetation. Only in the polar regions can so few species of plants be found in such a large expanse.

East of the Sahara, across the Red Sea, is the Arabian Desert, which covers most of the Arabian Peninsula. Moving eastward from the Arabian Desert one finds the Great Indian or Thar Desert located in western India. North of the Thar lie the Iranian, the Turkestan and the Takla Makan deserts.

In south-western Africa the Kalahari Desert supports a plant growth that is rather lush by desert standards. Grass grows there in some quantity and there is sufficient plant and animal life to support the primitive Bushmen, who live off the products of the land. The Kalahari extends west to what is known as the Namib Desert—an extremely dry, yet sometimes foggy, coastal desert, with actual rainfall of only one or two inches a year. Dew, about which we will have more to say later, may play an important part in supplying moisture for plant growth in this desert. Second in size of the world's deserts is the Australian, which occupies over forty per cent of the central and western portions of that continent.

In South America are two major desert areas. The Monte-Patagonian stretches as a narrow strip from central South America to the south-eastern coast of Argentina. The Atacama-Peruvian Desert stretches along the Pacific coast, and is shared by Chile and Peru; it has the distinction of being the driest of all the world's deserts. Like the Namib, its coastal areas tend to be foggy.

The North American desert, which lies in the south-western portion of the United States and extends down into Mexico, has four main

(below, left)
Some desert areas are young geologically; their rocks and hills are scarcely worn down. In this picture delicate, pink **Indian paintbrush** blooms against a background of black lava rock, which has changed little since its formation.

(below, center)
South African desert areas burst into bloom with masses of yellow **thistles.** Like those of similar plants in other parts of the world, the fruits have hooks or barbs that catch in the fur of animals, sometimes spreading the seeds in this manner.

(below, right)
In western Australia near Mount Gibson the desert is vivid with blossoming herbs. Shown in this picture is **myriocephalus,** which justifies its botanical name, "many-headed."

THE AUSTRALIAN DESERT

TRICHINIUM

MACROPIDIA

CARPOBROTUS

ANIGOZANTHUS

BLANCO CANESCENS

ISOPOGON (*Protea*)

Much of western and central Australia is desert land, constituting the world's **second largest desert.** In this vast region, somewhat like the American Southwest, red mountains rise above parched river beds, and yellow brush brightens the long sand ridges that edge the horizon.

divisions: the Great Basin Desert, the Chihuahuan, the Mojave and the Sonoran.

The Great Basin is the largest of these; it covers most of Utah and Nevada, and extends into parts of California, Oregon, southern Idaho and Wyoming. This is an arid upland, most of it more than 4,000 feet above sea level, and it is less hot than the other North American deserts. Its winters are cold, and most of its four to eleven inches of precipitation falls in the winter—some of it in the form of snow. This desert is characterized by low-growing shrubs, of which sage is one of the best-known.

The Chihuahuan Desert covers much of north-eastern Mexico and

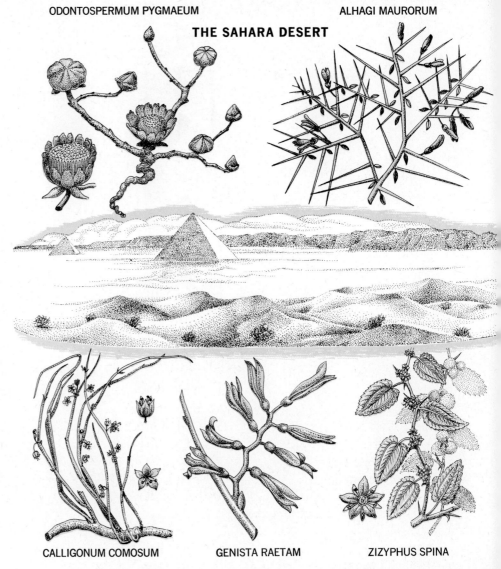

ODONTOSPERMUM PYGMAEUM

ALHAGI MAURORUM

THE SAHARA DESERT

CALLIGONUM COMOSUM

GENISTA RAETAM

ZIZYPHUS SPINA

To an Arab the word *sahara* means desert, and so, when we say "Sahara Desert," we are really saying "Desert Desert." But perhaps this is not as silly as it sounds, for the **Sahara** is indeed the **desert of deserts.** It is the largest in the world and covers more than three million square miles of African land. Throughout the centuries it has fascinated or terrified the traveler, for to cross its vast expanse by land even today requires great stamina and a firm knowledge of desert conditions and how to cope with them.

spreads into south-western Texas with tentacles reaching well into the state of New Mexico. The greater part of this desert lies above 3,500 feet, and receives most of its moisture during the summer months. Characteristic plants of this rather high, cool desert are shrubs and succulent plants such as agaves and yuccas.

The Mojave is a small desert bridging the gap between the Great Basin Desert on the north and the Sonoran Desert on the south. This Mojave Desert country flows across portions of southern California and southern Nevada with a small extension into north-western Arizona. Receiving only two to five inches of rainfall a year, with summer rainfall almost nonexistent, lying at elevations from approximately 4,000 feet down to almost sea level, this is a shrubby desert

(right)
One of the most familiar of the desert shrubs, **sage** can be found in the Great Basin, which is the largest division of the North American desert. Situated about 4,000 feet above sea level, the Great Basin is cooler than the other parts of the North American desert, and its winters are cold.

(above)
The unusual form of the **Joshua tree** is a result of its tendency to expand in a new direction wherever a blossom cluster forms. In California, the Joshua Tree National Monument contains forests of these trees.

characterized by creosote bush and by the weird and wonderful Joshua tree, its outstanding native.

The Sonoran Desert is the most interesting of the North American deserts because its varied climatic conditions and topography enable it to support considerable varieties of plants and animal life. The Sonoran Desert surrounds the head of the Gulf of California radiating from there into southern California, southern Arizona and extending down into lower California and Mexico. In elevation it lies below 3,500 feet and winters are mild. The eastern portion of this desert has both a summer and winter rainfall; but the western section, which is notorious for its very hot summers, receives its very limited rainfall only in the winter. The giant saguaro cactus is the "hallmark" of the Sonoran Desert, but some parts of it support a rich number of plant forms including small trees, cacti, shrubs and small flowering plants.

Desert Topography Varies

THE DESERTS WE FIND on the earth today are thought to be of relatively recent creation—new, that is, compared with the great age of the earth itself; they are no more than approximately one to 5 million years of age, and the faces of some of them are still young. They are broken by jagged mountain ranges and grooved by dry stream beds. These deserts' rugged outlines are sharp and clear, for no heavy cover of vegetation obscures or softens them. And in those deserts where there is a variety of habitats, from low mountaintops to gravelly slopes, from sandy plains to dry stream bed fringes, an increasing variety of plants can grow, each settled in the conditions which suit it best. The Sonoran is an example of such a desert that provides a wide variety of habitats, and which is therefore able to support an interesting assortment of plant types.

Some deserts, however, have been ground down to a near flatness by ages of wind, water and heat working methodically upon them. And where little variety of habitat is provided the number of plant forms to be found is decreased, as in a large portion of the Sahara.

Some Desert Plants Exhibit Parallel Evolution

THE DESERT ENVIRONMENTS since their inceptions have placed certain limiting conditions upon the plant growth found originally in each of these areas. Of all these conditions, heat and aridity have been of primary importance. Over great periods of time this original plant stock in each desert environment has evolved, adapting itself to these particular living conditions. Those that met with success in this process survived as a group, and so today we find plants specially suited for life in a desert environment. Indeed, many of these plants could not survive if removed from their desert setting and placed in what our agrarian-oriented minds would consider a more "favorable" environment.

In this evolving process oftentimes plants not closely related, and living in widely separated desert areas of the world, developed similar adaptations for coping with desert situations. These plants, then, which have evolved similarly, bear a superficial resemblance to each other. This process is known as parallel evolution and is seen in animals as well as plants. For example, cacti, native to the Western Hemisphere and living in arid areas, have developed succulent stems for storing water. At first glance they bear a striking resemblance to certain euphorbia plants of Africa which also have developed large succulent stems for water storage. Phylogenetically the relationship of the cacti and euphorbias is not a close one—superficially they would appear to be near relatives.

Desert plants, then, regardless of the desert in which they grow, have been faced with certain similar environmental conditions and have, through ages of time, evolved a series of similar methods of dealing successfully with these conditions. How, then, do they meet and beat the desert heat, aridity and related unfavorable conditions for growth? This subject is what we propose to explore in regard to the flowering plants of the deserts.

Xerophytes

PLANTS WHICH ARE ESPECIALLY ADAPTED for growing under arid conditions are referred to as xerophytes or as xerophytic plants. Xerophytes can generally be divided into two main groups known as drought evaders and drought resisters, dependent upon the methods they have evolved for living under desert conditions. Drought evaders

Reaching as high as three feet, these **penstemons,** or beardtongues, bloom in the spring and early summer throughout the southwestern United States. Colorful perennials, they range in color from blue to scarlet.

THE SONORAN DESERT

CALABAZILLA   ASTRAGALUS   ARGEMONE

LARREA MEXICANA   ENCELIA   DATURA STRAMONIUM

The greatest variety of desert plants in North America occurs in the **Sonoran Desert** of southern California, southern Arizona and Mexico. Below 3,500 feet in elevation, it has varied weather conditions and topography.

are opportunists. They have best met the problems of drought by not meeting it at all—at least not directly. The drought evaders are annuals, and it is these which produce the luxuriant crop of wild flowers that carpet the desert soil in favorable years and for which the deserts are justly famous.

The drought evaders, annuals such as the desert dandelion, desert sunflower, sand verbena, evening primrose and hundreds of others, spend most of the year as seeds hidden in and on the desert floor. But when suitable conditions of moisture and warmth reach them they rapidly germinate, grow, flower and produce seed. This they do in a matter of a few weeks before the conditions that have triggered their growth can disappear. Because they pass through the major part

(above, left)
Bright additions to spring flower displays, **lupines** are members of the pea family. Like others of that family, they obtain nitrogen from the air and fix it in the soil, improving the land in which they grow. Some lupines are called bluebonnets; in Texas the bluebonnet has been selected as the state flower.

(above, right)
Acacias are shrubs or trees, mainly tropical or subtropical in their distribution, and many species are found in dry regions. Nearly three quarters of the six hundred kinds of acacia occur in the deserts or semi-arid regions of Australia. There they are known as "wattle" because they are used with mud for building temporary sheepfolds and shelters ("mud and wattle" construction). Other acacias can be found in the Americas and Africa.

of their life cycle, from germination to the production of a new generation of seed, so quickly, they are referred to by some botanists as "ephemerals"; this word, which literally means confined to a day, is something of an exaggeration in this application. With the ephemeral desert plants the cycle of growth often takes approximately six to eight weeks, although some desert plants manage it in four weeks. The record speed, however, is probably that attributed to a plant of the Sahara, *Boerhaavia repens*, which has been reported to have required only eight to ten days between germination and seed production. So the term "ephemeral" is not, in this case, a very wild exaggeration!

Certain environmental conditions must be present before the seeds of these annuals will germinate; and the same conditions act as an assurance that at least minimum requirements for growth will be met for these plants once germination does take place.

Depending upon their environmental situation, certain species of ephemerals may grow well, reach maximum size, flower profusely and produce plentiful seeds; or these same species under adverse conditions may barely maintain life, achieve only a limited size, flower sparingly and produce few seeds. For example *Sphaeralcea coulteri*, a member of the mallow family found in the Sonoran Desert, may mature at a height of a few inches or may reach a height of nine feet. This ability of certain ephemerals to reach maturity, even when conditions are such that they cause the plants to be of dwarf size, is an indication of their hardiness and adjustment to rigorous conditions.

Seeds of Annuals

SEEDS ARE AMAZING and intricate pieces of living matter. Each one carries within it the means of producing a duplicate of its own

(left)
Evening primroses evade the drought by remaining underground in seed form much of the year. When conditions are suitable—that is, when warmth and water reaches them—they germinate, grow and flower. Their large, delicate four-petaled flowers are white or yellow, turning pinkish with age.

parent plant. Given the proper conditions it will germinate, and eventually fulfill the promise it carries.

The seeds of the desert annuals lie dormant within the soil sometimes for as long as several years. But when certain environmental conditions are met these seeds are triggered into action, and germination and growth take place. A foremost requirement is water. Interesting experiments have shown, however, that germination will not occur unless the moisture available is sufficient to "guarantee" that the plant will be able to grow successfully. A slight shower, providing insufficient water to support growth of the plant to maturity, would not set off this action.

If a seed is lying in the soil at a depth of only a fraction of an inch where it is located, a brief shower will make it no less wet than it would become as a result of several hours' rainfall. The question as to how seeds of the ephemerals could make the distinction between sufficient and insufficient soil moisture for growth intrigued scientists. The answer was found by an American botanist, Dr. Frits W. Went. He determined that there are chemical inhibitors present in the seed coats which prevent germination of these seeds. Only when the inhibitors have been washed away by moisture flowing down through the soil are these seeds capable of germinating, and sufficient water to remove the inhibitors was also approximately sufficient water to support growth of the resulting plant. Water rising from below, as by capillary action, does not trigger germination, for the inhibitory chemicals remain.

In some parts of the Sonoran Desert two periods of rainfall normally occur each year—a period of winter and one of summer rainfall. As a result there are two separate periods of flowering of the annual

(above)
Because small hairs on the plant are said to irritate the eye, **globe mallows** are often called "sore-eye poppies." The mallows range from single plants of a few inches in height to clumps of a hundred stems, each four to five feet tall. Occasionally a plant may reach nine feet, when environmental conditions are extraordinarily good.

THE SOUTH AFRICAN DESERT

ALOE

PUNCTILLARIA

EUPHORBIA

PACHYPODIUM

MONADENIUM

ADENIA

In southwestern Africa, the **Kalahari Desert** contains a relatively lush variety of plant life. It extends west to the coastal **Namib Desert,** an extremely dry area sometimes covered with fog.

plants; and most of the species which flourish following the winter rains are different from those which develop after the summer rainfall. Clearly, if the assurance of adequate moisture for proper growth were the only condition necessary for the plants to come to life such a distinction between the flora at different times should not exist; it seems that temperature, too, must play an important part in the triggering action.

Experiments have shown that seeds of the winter annuals will not sprout if the soil temperature is too high; and the summer annuals remain dormant in cool soil even when it is generously moistened. A soil temperature in the range of 60 to 65 degrees suits the winter plants, whereas the summer flora demands 80 to 90 degrees. The exceptions are a few tolerant species which can be found at both times.

Seed Dispersal in Time

THE CONTINUED EXISTENCE of any species of plant depends on more than a successful sprouting of its seeds; it depends on the successful maturing of the new generation so that it, too, produces a supply of seed. In the desert nature gives no very certain guarantee that this will always be possible, and if *all* the seeds of a species sprout at once there is an ever-present possibility of a sudden and exceptional change in conditions which would nip a whole generation in the bud.

Studies have shown that certain plants, such as some species of the genus *Atriplex*, have an inbuilt protection against this kind of disaster; they regularly produce two types of seeds—one kind which is capable of germination soon after being shed and another which requires a longer period of waiting before being able to germinate. An annual, *Salsola volkensii*, studied in Israel, was found to produce both green and albino dispersal units. The green units were capable of germination under a variety of conditions soon after being shed, but after three years were no longer viable. The albino units, after release from the parent plant, would germinate only under very limited temperature conditions. The ability of this second group to germinate increased with age, however, so that they were reaching the height of their ability to germinate at the time when the first group was becoming sterile. Thus germination of the seeds of this plant is spread over a period of time as an insurance against mass failure or destruction due to environmental conditions.

The North American **bear grass** looks like other yuccas, but its very narrow leaves are split at the tip and not pointed, and the individual flowers are much smaller. It is also known as Spanish bayonet.

The ability of seeds to remain viable over long periods of time is a great asset to a desert annual. An ephemeral, in order to be successful, must not start its growth until environmental conditions are suitable, and under exceptionally severe desert conditions such opportunities may be as rare as once in several years. Yet many of these seeds remain viable during these inhospitable times and grow to maturity when the opportunity at last arrives.

Seed Survival in Deserts

EVEN THE MANNER in which a desert plant sends forth its seeds may serve a survival purpose. Some desert annuals have developed a method whereby large numbers of seeds are produced and these are equipped to go "travelling". That is, they may be specially constructed with "wings" or other adaptations so that they are carried by wind, water, animals or other factors, some distance away from

The **goldpoppy,** sometimes called desert poppy or cloth-of-gold, is an annual that blooms in great abundance following winters of adequate rainfall.

the parent plant. The fact that so many are produced, and scattered in so many directions and at such varied distances provides a reasonable guarantee that at least some of them will find the right conditions for their development.

Other desert plants rely on methods of dispersal which give their seeds some guarantee of being able to germinate in the same location as that in which the parent plant has managed to thrive.

An interesting example can be seen in plants which will not release their seeds until rain falls on them and ensures the quick attachment of the seeds to the local soil. Certain desert annuals of the genus *Plantago* have been reported from Israel in which the seed is retained on the plant and is enclosed by the bracts or leaves of the floral axis. With the drying of the plant these seed coverings become hard and woody, but with the coming of rain the coverings curve outward and release the seed to fall near the parent plant on freshly moistened soil.

Some seeds of the kind which require water for their release from the parent plant are covered with a material which becomes sticky when wet. Consequently, when they reach the ground they tend to be held wherever they fall—and this is generally very close to the spot which suited the previous generation—and which can be expected to suit the new one, too.

Such adaptations can provide a plant with just the slight advantage that makes all the difference between success and failure.

When conditions are advantageous, desert annuals often grow to form large, bright-hued blankets on the sandy soil. Sand may not be thought to be a very promising material; but it is very suitable for many ephemerals. It is porous and enables water to soak into it, rather than run off it. Its surface catches wind-blown seeds, sifting over them, and holding them there until growing conditions are right. And in the spring the surface of the sand warms rapidly, acting as an incentive to growth.

Ephemerals may be found clustered in depressions in the soil where their seeds have lodged and where extra moisture has gathered. Seeds may lodge and ultimately grow where stones or larger rocks scattered about the surface of the soil offer them some protection from the wind. Larger plants, too, provide a measure of protection from wind and sun, so that the rate of evaporation of soil moisture close to them is lower than elsewhere. As a result there is a likelihood that annuals will

Areas of sand, sterile much of the year, support an impressive array of annuals when sufficient moisture is available. Because sand is porous, rain can soak into it, and the surface of the sand warms quickly in the spring, providing a choice location for these vivid, short-lived plants.

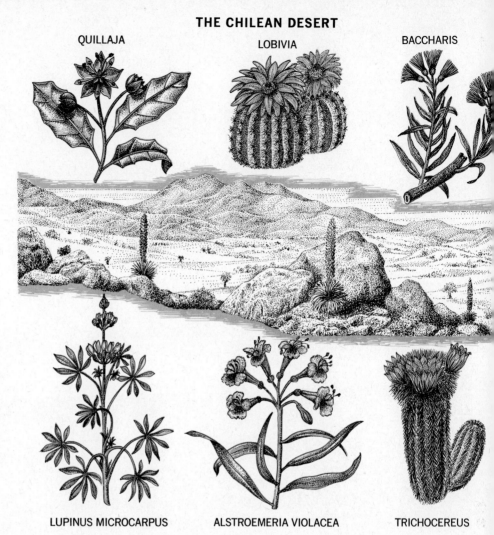

THE CHILEAN DESERT

QUILLAJA

LOBIVIA

BACCHARIS

LUPINUS MICROCARPUS

ALSTROEMERIA VIOLACEA

TRICHOCEREUS

Driest of the world's deserts, the **Atacama Desert** of Chile is a forbidding place for most natural life. Its vast wasteland has earned it the name "the valley of the moon." Nevertheless, certain plants have been able to exist here, and sometimes to thrive.

be found growing relatively more densely close to these larger plants that in other more "open" desert sites.

Where man has entered the desert and disturbed the soil, certain annuals such as prickly pear, glovemallow and desert marigold may grow more profusely. This is especially true along roadsides; wherever the artificial disturbance of the soil has led to the formation of furrows or cracks seeds are likely to be trapped, and can be expected to thrive.

The Success of the Ephemerals

As ARIDITY INCREASES, the percentage of annuals making up the total flora of the environment increases. There is a simple reason for the relatively higher rate of success of the desert ephemerals. It is not that these plants have drastically changed their form, like some of the desert perennials, in order to live in the very arid conditions of the desert. Their success is more or less assured just because their

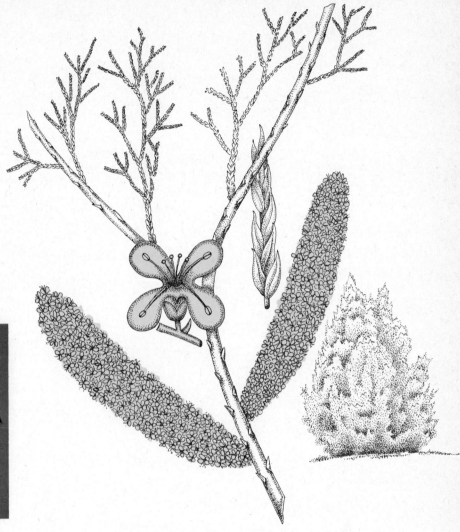

(below)
The **datura** belongs to the same large family as tobacco, belladonna, tomato, eggplant, red pepper and potato. All have large, single, erect flowers.

(above)
Although native to the Eastern Hemisphere, **tamarisk trees** have been successfully introduced into other parts of the world, including the southwestern United States. These trees thrive in saline soils in hot climates and may form dense stands along stream beds.

active life span is so short that it can be completed even if the conditions which are necessary for their growth pass very quickly.

The intricate checks and balances within the seeds that prevent them from premature germination yet ensure their rapid sprouting and growth when the proper time arrives; the hardiness of the seeds that lie in the desert and are subjected to extreme conditions such as heat; the retention of viability in these seeds for long periods; and special seed dispersal mechanisms—all of these are adaptations that aid the ephemerals in coping successfully with their desert environment.

Perennials

THE DESERT AT MIDDAY in the height of summer is one of the loneliest places on earth. The bright sunlight bleaches the vast terrain, causing heat waves to dance in the distance and oppressive heat to engulf whatever living thing may find itself there. At such a time the desert animals, although present, have apparently disappeared. Most of them are underground where the insulating soil protects them from the heat. Others rest in whatever shade the sparse desert vegetation can provide. Animals and men can take active measures to avoid the heat of the desert. Not so the plants, which must submit to what the desert has to offer where they stand. We have already seen how the drought-evading ephemerals are equipped to succeed in completing their essential role in the unending struggle of these species for survival. But what of those plants whose individual lifetimes are longer than a single season? How do these survive the desert climate? They employ many means, and these we will be discussing. However, to understand the special adaptations these drought-resisting plants have made to their dry and hot environment we must first understand how an "average" plant uses water in a more normal environment.

The Necessity of Water

IN THE COMPLETE ABSENCE OF WATER, there is complete absence of plant life. Water is a vital necessity for the maintenance of life. A plant's roots, probing underground, absorb water, which is carried through the roots into the plant portions above the ground. The water is moved through tubes in the plant structure, which carry it to every part of the plant. Ultimately the water is returned to the atmosphere by the slow evaporation process called "transpiration". There is a steady streaming of water, therefore, from the roots to the farthest reaches of the plant. It is the movement of water within the plant, and not its mere presence, that is a vital necessity if the plant is to thrive.

Water provides a transport system within the plant, as it brings dissolved nutrients with it into the plant and carries these materials essential for growth in solution to all parts of the plant. Chemical reactions within the plant take place in a liquid medium. Water is an essential raw material in photosynthesis, the manufacture of food for plant growth. Water is of prime importance in helping the plant maintain a fairly constant temperature and in keeping the plant temperature below lethal levels. And, finally, it is the maintenance of myriads of thin-walled individual cells in a "swollen" state by internal water pressure that gives the plant its rigidity.

Photosynthesis—the Manufacture of Food

WITHOUT PLANT LIFE no animal life could exist, for plants are the food manufacturers of the world. In the vital process of food manufacture known as photosynthesis water is indispensable. Water, composed of hydrogen and oxygen, enters a plant through its roots and is "pumped" into the stems and leaves. Within the protoplasm of the plant are small green bodies called chlorophyll bodies. In the

The **Joshua tree** differs from most other species of yucca in having numerous branches, each terminating in a dense bunch of short, spinelike leaves. The greenish-white flowers grow in a huge, tight cluster at the tip of each leaf branch.

THE IRANIAN DESERT

PHLOMIS VISCOSA

ANABASIS ARTICULATA

VARTHEMIA IPHINOIDES

(left)
Two vast and almost uninhabitable deserts cover more than 38,000 miles of Iran. They are called the Dasht-i-Lut and the Dasht-i-Kavir. Much of Iran, or former Persia, is dry. Only one navigable river, the Karun, exists. The other streams flow into central Iran and dry up in the salt and sand deserts.

(below)
Protoplasm, carrying chlorophyll bodies, moves within the plant cell. This diagram shows the protoplasm (2) and the direction in which it moves (6). The plant cell's outer membrane (1) also encloses cavities (3), the nucleus (4) and the nucleole (5).

ACACIA RUDDIANA

THYMELAEA HIRSUTA

ZYGOPHYLLUM DUMOSUM

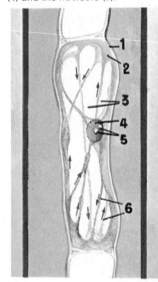

presence of this chlorophyll, with the sun's energy providing the power, the water is split into its components of hydrogen and oxygen. Some of the oxygen passes out of the plant through *stomata*, or breathing pores, in the plant's leaves. In through these stomata comes carbon dioxide from the atmosphere. The "surplus" hydrogen, left from the splitting of the water molecule, combines with the carbon dioxide, which entered through the stomata, to form a sugar. Simple as the process has been made to seem by this brief description, countless attempts to duplicate the action of photosynthesis in laboratory experiments have failed.

(top, left)
The many species of North American **agave** store water in their leaves. The larger species are called **century plants** or mescals. Although they have unusually long life spans, they rarely last a full century. Beautiful masses of flowers are raised high on a stalk by each plant just once; then the entire plant dies.

(top, center)
In the spring the desert **mariposas** make a gorgeous display. Whole acres of desert are often carpeted with mariposas after a rainy period. Their blossoms range in color from yellow to red and from white to lavender; stems vary in height from a few inches to a foot.

(top, right)
Named state flower of Utah, the **sego lily** has provided food as well as beauty. The bulbs from which they are grown were eaten by the Navajo and Hopi Indians.

Transpiration

T HE "BREATHING PORES" on a plant's leaves, the stomata, through which oxygen-carbon dioxide exchange takes place, are usually more numerous on the undersides of leaves; they are often present in enormous numbers. Each stoma is controlled by two bean-shaped guard cells. When water is present in the plant in quantity these cells swell up. As the cells are thicker at their ends, this swelling has the effect of forcing the inner edges of the two cells, near the mid-point, away from each other, causing a small opening or "mouth" to appear. At this time, then, gases may enter through these in order that photosynthesis may be carried on, and also water vapor will escape through them. When the cells relax, through a reduction of internal water pressure (because of a fall in temperature or because of a sheer lack of water) or through lack of daylight, the stoma closes.

The process whereby water vapor is lost from a plant through its stomata is known as transpiration. Water enters through the roots, serves one or more functions as it passes through the plant, and then most of it is lost through this process of transpiration. As an indication of the importance of the mechanical role of water in a plant it can be mentioned that as little as *one part in a thousand* of all the water in it might be tied up in chemical compounds at any one time. In some kinds of vegetation enormous amounts of water are returned to the atmosphere every day. It is estimated that a single acre of maize may transpire approximately 300,000 gallons of water in a growing season! Most desert perennials lack such water resources, and not all the methods by which they manage to survive are as yet clearly understood.

"Bi" is the native Bushman name for a plant which grows in the Kalahari Desert. When conditions become too harsh, all the parts of the plant which are above the ground wither and die; but, beneath the surface, the large tuber from which the plant grows, and in which moisture and food is stored, continues to live; when conditions able to support growth return, the plant will spring to life once more, drawing on the food reserves in the tuber—so long as the Bushmen have not used it for their own purposes! For the local people are well aware of its value, and have discovered in the bi tuber a reliable provider of moisture in this arid land.

Many other plants of the world's deserts have adopted this plan of retreat but not complete surrender in the face of the deserts' extremes. Plants such as the North American mariposa lily could easily be mistaken for small bright annuals at first glance; for when given proper conditions, they appear on the desert's surface briefly, bloom and then apparently die. In reality only their upper portions die; underground, their life continues at a reduced tempo and they will produce new stems, leaves and flowers when conditions are right again.

Succulents—Water Storage Plants

IN ADDITION TO THOSE PLANTS that store moisture underground, there are others which are able to retain sufficient water in their above-ground parts to avoid the destruction of the "open-air" structures. Cacti are a classic example. This group of plants has almost completely done away with leaves. When these are present it is usually only when the plant first germinates and begins growth, or—in the case of some cacti—for short periods on the new joints; for example the prickly pears, members of the genus *Opuntia*. The main parts of a cactus plant are its stem and branches; it is in these that the process of photosynthesis, normally a function of a plant's leaves, is carried on. This stem is capable of storing large amounts of water and actually expands and contracts with its water supply. This stored water, in addition to other adaptations they have made, effectively allows the cacti to survive extended periods of drought.

Closely resembling cacti, although not closely related to them, are species of plants belonging to the family *Euphorbiaceae,* known as euphorbias, which can be found growing in arid areas in southern Africa. These too have adapted to conditions of water shortage by developing thick, succulent stems and branches—and their leaves are very small, or have become nothing more than small excrescences. Spines are usually present on these plants.

Other plants may store water in their succulent leaves. Among American plants the agaves are a good example; their leaves are huge, grey-green, and stiff, and grow in a rosette about a central, subterranean stem. The leaves of some species may be six feet or more in length, with spiny edges and a sharp, strong spine at the tip. Agaves are slow growing, and usually do not put up a flower stalk until they are twenty or thirty years old—and sometimes very much older; eighty years, and even 120 years have been claimed as possible ages before blossoming. The flowering stalk grows in a single season and may be twenty or thirty feet tall. It bears at its top a huge, often branching cluster of funnel-shaped flowers. After this single burst of

The bright red flowers that appear at the tips of the **ocotillo plant** stems have inspired the common names of candlewood and flamingsword. Ocotillos grow in the southwestern United States and in Mexico.

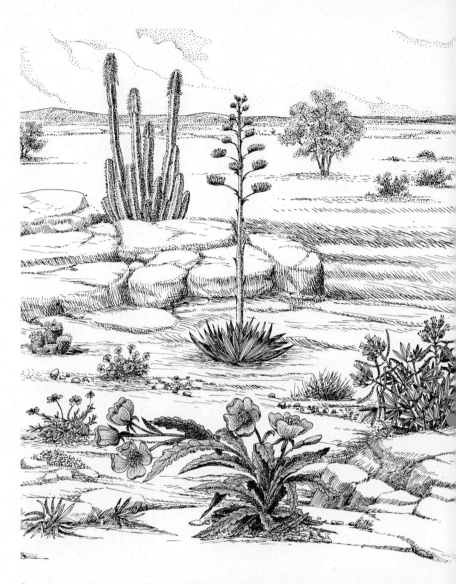

flowering glory the plant usually dies. The century plants, which are so-called because of the mistaken notion that they do not bloom until they are a hundred years old, and mescals, are among the larger species; they have yellow flowers, often tinged with purple, which grow upwards in clusters from flat horizontal panicles. *Agave lechuguilla,* a smaller species, with stiff-spined, black-tipped, greyish leaves, covers hundreds of square miles in the desert lands of Texas and New Mexico, and is one of the most typical plants of the Chihuahuan Desert. Its flowers are lavender-brown.

Water-seekers

A TREE ASSUMES A SPECIAL IMPORTANCE, in one sense, when it grows in a desert; and this is not because it has a "rarity value".

A number of plants grow in the areas bordering desert washes. After a rainfall, water is present in the washes for a brief period; underground water is also more likely to be found in these areas. Along the stream beds, small trees, shrubs and other plants often form strips of vegetation, standing out in contrast to the more arid, overall landscape of the desert.

In the desert the presence of a tree is usually a signal that there is a supply of water near it, at least during a part of the year, even though the water may be quite some distance away.

If a desert area is capable of supporting any trees, these are often found along usually dry water courses. When rain does fall in a desert the run-off collects in these *wadis,* washes, or whatever the dry stream beds happened to be called locally. It is in such sites that moisture is most likely to be found trapped underground. The trees that grow in them survive not by storing water, as the cacti do, but by developing a long tap root which can reach deep enough to draw on the water supply. This tap root is augmented by lateral roots, closer to the surface, which also take advantage of any moisture which may be available from time to time in the upper soil levels.

One of the most conspicuous of the early blooming plants of the American Southwest, the **brittlebush** is a hardy perennial, partly because of its ability to poison most of the plants that try to grow nearby. The low, grey-green hemispherical shrubs are covered by bright yellow flowers, each raised two or three inches above the leaves.

The mesquite tree is a good example. This tree of the North American deserts may grow as a shrub, or as a quite considerable tree. It is a first-class indicator of underground water and the tap roots of mesquites have been known to stretch to depths of 100 feet to reach a water source, while lateral roots radiate far and wide near the surface. In the spring small leaflets appear, and the tree blossoms with yellow flowers in cylindrical "spikes". The seed pods which follow are from four to eight inches long, and they resemble string beans. The limbs tend to be twisted and gnarled. Where sufficient water is available, mesquite trees sometimes form dense thickets eventually, and individual trees may grow to be as much as fifty feet tall, with twisted and gnarled limbs.

The mesquite was a blessing to the American Indians and pioneers, because it provided house-building material, firewood, fence posts and raw material for a series of everyday utensils. It was also a source of food; for the pods and seeds were eaten raw or cooked, or ground into a flourlike meal, and they could be fermented to make alcohol. The large stands of mesquite were so exploited by the early settlers and those who followed them that, in the United States today, most of the stands of the larger mesquites have disappeared.

The mesquite seed is equipped with a very hard covering which indirectly helps to ensure that they become distributed. The seed pods are eaten by cattle, and after passing through the cattle, are eventually returned to the soil over a considerable range. Not only are the seeds unharmed—they are actually helped by this process, because the animals' digestive juices weaken the hard covering and provoke their germination.

The mesquite in some areas is spreading out into the grasslands bordering the United States deserts' deteriorating rangeland. It has also been introduced into many other parts of the world where it was not native, and in many of these locations is today considered more of a blight than a boon.

There are some trees which grow in the desert, but which cannot possibly be defined as water seekers—they have made no special adaptations to help them to locate water—they simply grow there if plentiful water happens to be available. An example of such a tree is the date palm. These palms are a welcome sight for the traveller in the Sahara where their green signifies an oasis. Date palms need large quantities of water, and so grow only in an oasis-type setting. They may be associated in our minds with the "image" of a desert, for a variety of reasons—but they are not characteristic of typical desert country because they cannot survive in really arid conditions.

Desert Plants Are Spaced Apart

IN LOOKING OUT OVER THE DESERT one immediately becomes aware of the sparseness of the vegetation. The reason for this sparseness is a very simple one. Once a plant has become established in an area of very scanty water there is very little left for any competitors to draw upon—it sets up a virtual monopoly of the water supply in its immediate locality. New plants are unlikely to get a foothold within range of its root system. When plants are thus widely separated, with a great deal of bare ground between them, the vegetation is described as "open". The greater the degree of openness, the scantier, we may be sure, is the amount of available moisture in the area.

Large root systems, in proportion to the plant portions aboveground, are a characteristic of many desert plants. To obtain sufficient moisture to support themselves, these plants depend upon their ability to draw on the water resources of a large area, and develop extensive, monopolizing root systems to do so.

Some plants even indulge in chemical warfare to hold their property and water rights. The creosote bush, one of the most successful of the North American desert plants, being widespread in the Sonoran, Mojave and Chihuahuan deserts, is thought to secrete a poisonous substance from the root tips, inhibiting the growth of other plants within a certain distance. Thus the creosote bush is protected from overcrowding and is assured of having sufficient area around it from which it can gather moisture. The brittlebush is a hardy, large, bushy desert perennial that brightens North American desert hillsides in the spring with its yellow flowers raised high on stalks above the plant's greyish foliage. Recent studies have shown that its leaves poison most plants that attempt to grow near it. This ability of some plants to

(below)
Besides providing essential shade to the desert dweller or traveler, the **date palm** supplies a great many important products: food, wine and raw materials for thatching and woven goods.

(right)
Many Indians as well as settlers in North America have used **ephedra** plants to make tea, and so the plant has been called Mormon tea, Mexican tea and squaw tea. Found in dry areas, the leaves are reduced to tiny scales and the branches are greenish in color.

(above)
The **devil's-claw** is an annual with bright, showy flowers. Its name comes from the seed pod, which has long, hooked, clawlike horns. These "claws" attach themselves about the legs of larger animals and are thus carried about, spreading their seeds.

(below, left)
On some plants the stomata are protected by **hairs,** which shield them against the drying desert air. Under a microscope these hairs may appear to be unique structures themselves.

(below, right)
A resin or **wax covering** can be seen on many desert plants, such as the cactus. This coating, like the hairs, is a protection against the loss of too much moisture.

excrete substances, either through roots or other plant parts, toxic to other plants has recently been found in additional shrubs, such as guayule and brittlebush, and may be more common than is thought at the present time.

Modifications for Living with Aridity

APPEARANCES MAY BE DECEPTIVE—in fact the appearances of desert plants have been deceiving scientists for many years, and only fairly recently have they been discovering that certain modifications of desert plants do not always serve the purpose attributed to them. As a beginning, let us consider what some of these modifications are and then move on to some of the current facts and theories regarding them.

If water, or rather the lack of it, is the primary problem faced by a desert plant, then it is assumed that a desert plant, unless it is in the unusual position of having access to plenty of water, must be modified for conservation of its water supply. There are many modifications that would appear to be directed toward this end. Water is lost through the stomata and on some desert plants there is a reduced number of stomata. Stomata on some plants may at times be occluded by resin or wax. On some plants the stomata are sunk below the surface level of the leaf in grooves or pits, and are protected by overarching adjoining cells, or are partially guarded by hairs, all of which would help to protect these "water-losers" from currents of drying desert air moving over them.

Even when the stomata are closed there is still a small water loss constantly taking place from the surface of the plant. Some desert plants have leaves which are covered with a coating of resin or wax, or with a covering of hairs that give the plant a greyish appearance—this is to protect them against moisture loss. In other cases the cuticle or outer layer of the leaf is thickened, and the same purpose is served.

Most desert plants have small leaves and many of the plants have

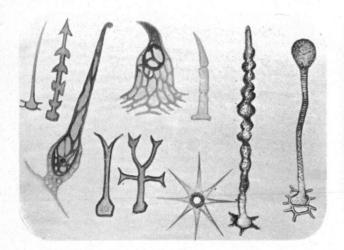

leaves that are heavily subdivided. Supposedly this affords a smaller leaf area from which water can be lost. Some leaves curl up or turn their narrow edges toward the sunlight, and this results in only a very small area being exposed to direct radiation. Other plants completely shed their leaves when aridity engulfs them as a means of cutting down water loss.

It had long been supposed that the special modifications of desert plants kept transpiration at a lower level than in other types of vegetation. Then, surprisingly, it was discovered that many nonsucculent desert perennials transpire more freely than mesophytes (plants which grow under moderately moist conditions) when water is equally available to them. Studies are now showing that when the xerophytic plants are in a hot, dry environment, small reductions of the transpiration rate have no value. The plant can better withstand the heating of its portions aboveground by transpiring freely to reduce its temperature, so long as sufficient moisture is available to replace what is lost. If water is too scarce for this, however, the plant can best prevent wilting by cutting transpiration to the lowest level possible, to retain such water as it contains. Any modifications in form which do drastically cut down the transpiration rate of a plant under this latter condition are then of value.

Closing of the stomata, of course, cuts transpiration to a minimum, but in order to avoid other small losses the plugging of the stomata with wax or resin as done by some plants, the sinking of the stomata into grooves, or other such modifications, would also logically be of help in reducing water loss. Small amounts of water can also be lost to the atmosphere through the leaves' surfaces and for this reason it has been thought that leaves equipped with thick cuticles would lose less moisture. No doubt the thickened cuticles do serve this purpose to some extent; but those plants which have heavy cuticular coverings are not necessarily those which lose the least water from the cuticle. However, such heavy cuticles have an important role not mentioned

(below)
Hummingbirds are particularly attracted to this handsome member of the sage family, and so it is called **hummingbird sage.** Sometimes a single plant bears as many as nine clusters of flowers.

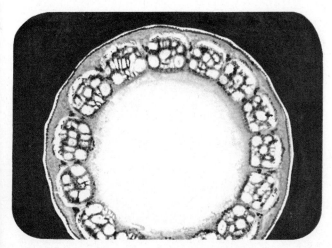

(left)
Thickened plant cuticles, as shown in this cross-section, not only protect the plant but also seem to help keep its temperature down. **Cutin** is a waxy substance that forms the chief ingredient of the cuticle in many plants.

so far; it is now believed that the extent to which they reflect sunlight helps to keep the temperature of the plant down. A similar function may be performed by the whitish hair coverings of some leaves; for some experiments have shown that this pubescence certainly does not significantly reduce transpiration, as was formerly believed. The presence of a waxy or oily coating on the surface of the leaves does reduce evaporation; laboratory tests have shown that if these materials are removed artificially the rest of water loss from the leaves increases very noticeably.

A rather common characteristic of many desert plants is small leaf size. It was thought that reduction in leaf size reduced the area from which transpiration could take place and was thus a water-saving device. But studies have shown that in some cases, though not all, the reduction in leaf size is more than compensated for by an increase in the number of leaves; and, hence, results in no reduction of the transpiration potential. Nevertheless, the reduction in leaf size is such a common characteristic of desert plants that it is thought it must play some significant role. The small size of the individual leaves does shorten the distance between the individual cells and the veins bringing moisture to these cells, which would be of value during moisture stress. This may also be an explanation for the leaves which are heavily subdivided. It may also be that the smaller size may be important in preventing overheating of the plant in direct sunlight.

Some desert perennials have leaves which change their form or

(below, left)
The abundance of leaves and flowers in the **ocotillo** pictured here is a sign that water is available. When water is scarce, this plant sheds its leaves in order to reduce transpiration (water loss).

(below, right)
The **blackfoot,** or desert daisy, is an attractive North American desert plant. These perennials usually grow on dry rocky slopes and produce vivid white flowers.

Ranging from purple to white in color, **phacelias** are found in the harsh environment of Death Valley. Like many other desert plants, its leaves are heavily subdivided, which may aid the plant during moisture stress.

their attitude during times of stress, so that less leaf area is exposed to the sunlight or to the drying atmosphere; this appears to be a protective device. However, this may be a more complicated matter than it first appears, since it occurs in some plants when loss of water by transpiration is not at its greatest.

Some plants of the desert have leaves only for short periods and when moisture conditions are such as to allow the plant to accept the higher rate of transpiration that results. The complete shedding of leaves is a very effective method of cutting down transpiration. The ocotillo is a strange-looking plant consisting of numerous long, straight, usually unbranched stems rising from a common point at ground level. The stems may be as much as twenty feet long, and the plant takes the shape of an inverted cone. When moisture is available, the ocotillo quickly puts forth many small green leaves along the entire length of the stems. At certain times each stem also produces at its tip a group of bright red flowers. Later, when water becomes scarce, the leaves are quickly shed, leaving only the leafless stems armed with spines to await the next rains. The ocotillo can amazingly produce several complete sets of leaves in a year—if moisture becomes available that many times. The ocotillo therefore crowds its growing, supported by the photosynthesis carried on by its leaves, into those periods when the leaves are present. When they are discarded, the ocotillo enters a resting state and awaits the next rains.

Palo verde means "green stake" in Spanish and is the name given by the Mexican people to another strange desert plant. This is a graceful, small tree which literally is a "green stake", for its trunk and limbs are green with chlorophyll. This plant, too, has leaves briefly during favorable periods, but even then the leaves are extremely small. When water becomes scarce the tiny leaves are shed and the tree carries on photosynthesis at a reduced rate with the chlorophyll in its trunk and stems.

Xerophytes, as we have noted, will often transpire more water than mesophytes if such water is available. However, when very little water is available the xerophytes, through evolutionary modifications, are able to lower their transpiration rates and can survive under conditions that would cause wilting and death for the mesophytes.

Research is now proving, however, that more than adaptations of form are involved in this survival-under-stress ability. It appears that the perennial xerophytes have made physiological adjustments also; and these, too, help them to survive the lack of water which is a common occurrence in their own environment. Their protoplasm is apparently capable of enduring greater extremes of desiccation, without permanent injury, than that of other types of plants. Also, drought-resistant species of plants often have greater sap densities than other types of plants, which may also play a part. Xerophytes are characterized by small cells and this may be a factor that helps avoid the breakdown of the individual cell and its contents when wilting takes place, or when water is suddenly available and is rapidly replaced in the cells.

Whatever may prove to be the reasons, it is now apparent that physiologically the more drought-resistant desert plants are able to endure wilting and recover from it more readily than non-xerophytes. Many xerophytes are capable of losing a large percentage of their water, and yet recover if water again becomes available. Mesophytes can tolerate only relatively slight dehydration without injury.

The question of how plants survive in the desert has no simple answer. And the more that is learned about the special ability of these plants to live in the conditions which the desert provides, the more it becomes clear that the real answer is a very complex one.

The Creosote Bush

PLANTS FOUND IN THE DESERT may have none, one or several of the special adaptations to withstand aridity and heat which we have been discussing. The creosote bush is an example of one of the most highly successful desert plants and it combines a number of features valuable from the standpoint of desert survival.

The creosote bush is one of the most common of North American desert plants and is also found in parts of South America. Typically it covers vast areas in the more arid sections of the desert and occurs in almost pure stands. It is a much-branched shrub, usually about three or four feet tall, but sometimes grows as high as ten feet. Its leaves are small, and dark green. The plant as a whole has a light and airy look, seeming to lack substance, and casts little shadow on the hot desert surface. In the North American deserts in the spring it usually produces many small yellow flowers. Since pure stands of the bush cover such large areas it makes a spectacular display even though the individual flowers are small and inconspicuous. The flowers are followed by furry, white seed balls that often hang on all summer.

Creosote bushes have been known to survive for as long as five years without any rainfall whatever. This is an extreme example, but

Like the brittlebush, the **creosote bush** seems to owe its success to a poisonous substance that it secretes, preventing other plants from growing nearby. After a rainfall small yellow flowers appear, and white, furry fruits often hang on the plant for some time.

(left)
The **palo verde tree,** its trunks and stems yellowish-green with chlorophyll, produces large numbers of yellow flowers in the spring. During the long dry seasons the small leaves are shed, but the green stems carry on the process of photosynthesis and maintain life. The tree grows slowly, because the lack of leaves during much of the year reduces its food-making potential.

the creosote bush commonly prospers in desert conditions which few other plants can survive. The leaves are small, presenting a relatively small surface to absorb solar radiation. They are heavily covered with a waxy coating that helps to protect them from water loss. They are, however, evergreen, being shed only under conditions of what is, even for these plants, extreme drought. Then the older leaves are shed first. The younger, partially grown leaves, persist and although they may dry out and turn brown, they are able to resume their growth and functions when water is once again available.

The creosote bush produces many roots which very effectively seek out moisture in a great circle about the plant. The creosote bush also sends a tap root to greater depths to exploit any water supplies at a lower level. It is thought that this plant secretes a toxic substance through its root tips to prevent the growth of other plants in its immediate vicinity, thus garnering for itself the available water resources. This results in stands of creosote bushes neatly spaced apart, almost as though planted with mathematical precision.

When conditions become difficult, however, the protoplasm of the creosote bush has the extremely important ability to endure great extremes of dehydration without permanent injury resulting. This ability, in addition to the other attributes of the plant we have discussed, makes the creosote bush one of the most drought resistant of the higher plants.

(above)
The flowers of the **evening primrose** open in the evening and begin to wilt the following morning. Some species grow as flat mats, others as shrubby plants up to five feet in height.

Halophytes

A SPECIAL PROBLEM faced by plants in certain parts of the deserts is soil that is saline, or salty. The rainfall is not sufficient in some areas to leach away these excess salts as would happen in more moist regions. Also, oftentimes in deserts, water is drained by dry washes into a common lower area and here the water evaporates leaving behind accumulations of salts. These areas are often known as dry lakes, or by the Spanish word for "beaches", *playas*.

If the salt is excessive, plants will not grow in the soil. There are, however, some specialized plants, known as halophytes, which can

(top, left)
The **velvet-pod mimosa** is a shrub found in Arizona, Texas and Mexico. It produces long spikes of purplish-pink flowers.

(top, center)
Enlivening the landscape, the **desert marigolds** often display a crop of bright yellow flowers. Each flower grows on a single, slender stem. Sometimes this flower is called the paper daisy because the petals remain on for some time, becoming dry and bleached.

(top, right)
Prickly poppies, usually plain white yellow middles, are known as "cowboy's fried egg." The foliage is bluish-green and thistlelike. It grows commonly where the ground has been disturbed along dry roadsides or on overgrazed cattle ranges.

grow in soils with greater than average concentrations of salt. Some halophytes are able to accumulate a certain amount of these salts in the plant without injury; others are able to exclude from entry salts which would be harmful to them. One group has the ability to take up the salts and then subsequently to excrete them through glandular cells on the leaves, if the concentration of salts in the sap builds up to a high level. Tamarisk trees belong to this group; and these sometimes have a distinctly grey appearance because of the considerable amounts of recrystallized salt deposited on their exterior surfaces.

Dew

ONE MIGHT NOT NORMALLY ASSOCIATE dew with a desert environment, yet in some desert locations dew can be a more reliable source of water supply, both for plants and animals, than the very rare rainfall.

The air is never completely without water, even in the desert. The air is "dry" because such water as it contains is almost completely gaseous; and even in most deserts you would probably find that a glassful of ice water would become somewhat misted, or "dewed", on the outside—if it were held in the shade. This is because the amount of water which air can support in a gaseous state depends on the temperature of the air; if it is sufficiently cooled water droplets will condense. Heat is rapidly lost by radiation from the rocks, gravel and plants in the desert during the night. And by sunrise they can be so cool that the air in contact with them yields small but precious amounts of water as a deposit of droplets.

It has been established that there are some plants of the arid areas which absorb dew through their leaves, although not all plants will do this. It is also known that dew absorption by a plant is higher under dry soil conditions than under irrigation. It may also be that plants with roots near the surface of the ground use moisture derived from dew condensed on the surface of the soil. The mere presence of dew on the plant, even if not absorbed, may serve a useful purpose; its evaporation will require heat—and this process will mean that much less heat is available for raising the plant's temperature. Heating of the plant will be delayed, at least a little, when the sun rises.

Scientists have only rather recently realized the significance of this aspect of the desert environment, and much study of it remains to be done. Interestingly, it appears that people of long ago were aware of the value of dew and made use of it. On the Sinai Peninsula, in the Negev and in the northern Sahara, hundreds of gravel piles arranged in regular patterns have been found. It is believed now that these were specially erected to accumulate dew so that plants could be grown even in the absence of rainfall or "spontaneous" condensation. The use of dew, long forgotten by man, but perhaps regularly used by desert plants and animals, may assume increased importance to man in the future, as he searches for additional land on which to raise crops to feed the world's rapidly expanding population.

The Potential of the Desert

THE DESERTS OF THE WORLD have recently been receiving increased attention from scientists and governments, and there is a growing realization that even the deserts are, potentially, land which could be encouraged to yield food.

As a result of increased scientific investigation our knowledge of the desert environment is rapidly expanding.

Outstanding work has been done in Israel during the last few years; here it has been shown that remarkable results can be achieved by "gently coaxing nature" to work for man in the desert. Some of the most interesting results that have been achieved have involved no massive assault on the earth itself, no giant pipelines. This can encourage us to hope that at least some parts of the earth, as yet unchanged by the hands of men, might survive as "useful" yet with their essential nature unchanged.

It is to be hoped that there will always remain, unchanged, vast deserts where man may see and experience the powerful, elemental forces of nature at work—heat, cold, aridity, wind—and see clear-cut examples of their work. The results are especially apparent in the flowering plants of the desert which are interesting and outstanding because they have met the desert's terms successfully, and produced life and beauty in a harsh but handsome land.

The **smoke tree** grows along washes on the lower, frost-free areas of the desert in California, southern Arizona and northern Mexico. Sometimes it looks like a puff of smoke in the distance because of its silvery, usually leafless branches. In the early summer it is covered with purple flowers.

► *The remarkable plants that manage to grow with hardly any water.*

Cactus

ALTHOUGH TODAY CACTI can be seen growing anywhere in the world, from a single potted plant on a London window ledge to an impenetrable thicket covering acres of Australian land, they are native only to the New World. A dubious and much-argued exception to this are a few species of a mistletoe-like plant found mostly in Africa and probably introduced there.

Believed to be an offshoot of the ancestral rose, the cactus is a comparative newcomer to the world of plants. Undoubtedly no other living thing so characterizes the desert in people's minds as the cactus, and correctly so, for it has dramatically adapted itself to surviving in one of the world's most difficult and exacting places. This notion is further reinforced by the American cowboy film whose landscape is often liberally sprinkled with saguaros, the most spectacular example of Arizona flora.

The first impression received by the newcomer taking his initial walk in the southern Arizona desert where cacti are abundant is that of prickliness. Everything seems covered with needles. No wonder that, as someone once said, the most often heard sound in the desert is "ouch".

The word "cactus" comes from the Greek word *kaktus,* a label originally pinned to a spiny plant, probably the thistle. This pigeonhole was established by Linnaeus in the eighteenth century to house the few species of cacti then known to science. Since then the number of species has grown to thousands, with new kinds continually being discovered.

Divided into three main groups, or tribes, the cactus family is composed of over a thousand species. Shapes and sizes vary considerably, but spines of some type are characteristic. These may ward off many animals, but some birds, such as this **cactus wren** (top right), find the **prickly cholla** a safe place in which to build a nest. They fly in and out of the plants without suffering so much as a scratch.

(top)
Cactus flowers are alike in structure, although the plants from which they spring may differ greatly. This bright yellow bloom is produced by the *Parodia chrysacanthion,* which grows in Argentina. Like other members of its genus, the plant is small and globular.

(above)
Euphorbias, native chiefly to southern Africa, are remarkably similar in shape to cacti. However, they differ in most other characteristics.

What Is a Cactus?

SIMPLY PUT, a cactus is a xerophyte or drought-resistant plant. To elaborate further, it is a perennial succulent and it is spiny, being characterized by specialized organs called areoles from which the spines grow. All cacti are dicotyledons, which means that the seed on germination produces two or more seed leaves called cotyledons. Outside of these few restricting facts almost anything goes.

Anyone who has glanced even casually through an illustrated cactus book will be impressed by the fantastic variety of their shapes. They may grow as tall as eighty feet or be so small that you can hardly see them. They may look like trees, shrubs or vines. They may have one single fat stem like the barrel cactus, or a massive bunch of tall slender stems like some of the cerei, or they may grow in a round moundlike clump of a hundred prickly heads or more. They may have leaves and a few spines like the pereskia, or be fuzzy with spines like the cholla. Some look exactly as a cactus should, and some look like anything but a cactus.

They are not even consistent in the appearance of their spines. One kind of prickly pear can produce only small scattered bumps of tiny soft-looking bristles called glochids. Others also flaunt long wicked needles in addition to glochids. Some spines are hooked, others are straight. Some are smooth, others scaly. Some are papery, some wooly, and some look like feathers.

In other words, cacti are as varied as most things that inhabit our earth and for that reason, if for no other, they are fascinating.

Cousins Because of Their Flowers

CACTI ARE SIMILAR in one other important way, and that is in the anatomy of their flowers. One thing all botanists will agree upon is the fact that the anatomy of the flower is a stable enough characteristic to be used in the grouping of plants. Thus all cactus flowers are alike in their basic structure no matter how unlike the plants that produce them may appear to the eye. It is this that distinguishes the cacti from other succulents such as the African euphorbias, for instance, some of which look more like a cactus than many cacti.

Happily, besides being scientifically useful, cactus flowers possess extraordinary beauty. It is a constant surprise and delight when spring arrives and these forbidding and bizarre plants are suddenly bedecked with vivid and exotic waxlike blossoms. The ugly duckling comes into its own, even if only temporarily.

Contrary to other desert plants that may bloom only after a sufficient amount of rain, all cacti have a definite time of bloom determined by the seasons and independent of rainfall. However, some cacti bloom only at night, producing in the dark some of the most spectacular flowers to be seen anywhere.

How They Got that Way

Though practically no fossil cacti exist to show concretely how these peculiar plants might have developed, fortunately examples are growing today of very primitive cacti on through to the highly specialized forms inhabiting some of our deserts. So before our eyes, in living plants, we can see many of the steps that were thought to be taken through the centuries as a plant that was hardly a cactus at all became one that was completely a cactus.

Whether this slow process took place because as the climate changed the plant itself had to change in order to survive, or whether it happened as certain plants extended their range into increasingly arid regions, is still very much a matter of conjecture. Perhaps it was, in reality, a bit of both.

The cactus is supposed to be of relatively recent origin. The one fossil that has so far been discovered—of a prickly pearlike plant—dates from 60 million years ago and therefore is not as old as fossils of many other flowering plants.

Plants that Look like Cacti

It is one of the strange and as yet unsolved puzzles that native cacti are confined to the New World. It isn't that they fail to flourish elsewhere, for once man has introduced them to a new home across the seas, they grow so hardily that in some cases they seem about to take it over, as the prickly pear almost did in Australia.

(below, left)
Desert life is not always what it may seem. *Euphorbia globosa* looks so much like a cactus that only a trained eye could tell the difference.

(below)
Giant cacti stems tower over the landscape of the Mexican desert. Cacti are able to survive in such harsh environments as this, where they are a familiar part of the scenery.

(top left)
Related to the cacti, **sedums,** commonly known as **stonecrops** or **orpines,** have starlike flowers varying in color from white to green, yellow and orange. There are over 500 species distributed across Europe, Asia, Africa and the Americas.

(top center)
This **staghorn** is one of the tree chollas (pronounced "choyas"). The cholla cacti are armed with slender thorns of about an inch and a half. These spines are deceptive, since they are covered with a papery sheath.

(top right)
Found in northern Argentina, this **species of cereus** was discovered after Drs. Britton and Rose published their famous work on cacti. The genus was named in honor of Dr. Domingo Parodi, who was very much interested in the flora of that area.

Instead of evolving a cactus of their own, desert areas in other parts of the world have produced succulents that look very much like cacti but belong to quite a different clan altogether. In fact some, like certain of the euphorbias, are impossible for an untrained eye to distinguish from a true cactus. This turn of events is called parallel evolution and is perfectly illustrated by the American cerei and the tall-stem succulents of Africa.

To further confuse matters, none of the New World euphorbias inhabiting its deserts, of which an Arizona species, the limberbush, is a good example, changed into any other form, as did other plants. However in Africa a close relative of this same euphorbia developed a thick, leafless water-storing stem along with protective spines, and is very cactus-like indeed.

In Africa, too, a true cactus, the rhipsalis, is found. It has also been discovered in Madagascar and Ceylon. Is this Old World specimen an exception to the rule? In 1912 a diligent Frenchman published a paper after investigating these plants, stating that he believed them to be really American species. He attributed their presence in the Old World to migratory birds who ate the fruit in South America and crossed the ocean to drop the seeds in Africa.

Besides being unusual-looking, the rhipsalis has very uncactus-like habits. By means of air roots it fastens itself to tropical trees from which it receives no nourishment and therefore is not parasitic. The casual passerby, seeing its long thin trailing stems, would never dream that it was a cactus.

How Botanists Group Them

As HAS ALREADY BEEN MENTIONED, the order in which cacti are grouped indicates roughly the probable evolutionary steps of development that these plants took on the long road to adapting themselves to desert living. Almost fifty years ago two American botanists, Dr. N. L. Britton and Dr. J. N. Rose, under the auspices of the Carnegie

Institute, published a monumental four-volume work saying most of what has been said about cacti. Known familiarly as Britton and Rose, it is still the cactus fancier's Bible.

These two gentlemen divided the cactus family into three main groups which they called tribes. In the first tribe, labelled *Pereskieae*, they placed the woody trees, bushes and vines which grow in the tropics. For the most part .they are handsome plants sporting large glossy leaves and roselike flowers, and are much prized as ornamentals. Looking at this plant it is easy to see why the cactus is thought to have descended from the ancient rose. It is also thought to be the living counterpart of the original primitive cacti that long ago lived as ordinary plants in tropical forests. To this group has now been added the low matted groundcover found in Chile and Argentina, called *Maihuenia*, another plant that does not resemble the usual cactus.

Opuntieae is the second tribe, characterized by having glochids or tiny hairlike bristles. These often grow in clumps like minute pincushions out of which longer spines may or may not also grow. The stems and branches of these cacti are usually fleshy and much jointed. Except for one species they are ribless and they are never epiphytic, meaning that they do not grow in trees or other plants. To this group belong the cholla (pronounced choya) and the prickly pear.

The third and last tribe is *Cereae*, the largest group of the three. It also claims the tallest specimens. The cacti belonging to this group have no glochids and can be either terrestrial or epiphytic. The saguaro, the barrel cactus and the pincushion, all common to the south-western United States desert, belong to this group, as well as the caterpillar-

(below)
This **candelabrum cactus** belongs to the largest of the three tribes of cacti, which includes the tallest specimens. In the same group are the saguaro, the barrel cactus and the pincushion, all common to the southwestern United States, as well as the caterpillar-like cactus of lower California.

Cacti are native only to the New World, although they do well wherever they are introduced. Some plants native to other dry areas, like this *Euphorbia splendens* of Africa, resemble cacti but are really much different plants.

like cactus that sprawls over the sand in Lower California and the multi-stemmed cereus that grows in the Andes. The word "cereus" comes from a Greek word meaning torch and is given to this tribe because of the branching candelabra-like appearance of some of its members.

Where They Grow

IN ORDER TO UNDERSTAND this strange thing called a cactus, it is important to have some understanding of the land where it grows. In the New World, cactus and deserts go together as naturally as hot dogs and mustard in most people's minds.

Though deserts vary in appearance as do the cacti themselves, they have certain characteristics in common: heat, low humidity and less than twelve inches of annual rainfall. Their ground is bare, their mountains are rough and angular, their riverbeds are dry, and their rocks are eroded by windblown sand. When the rain comes, it is usually a violent thunderstorm or cloudburst that may drop the whole of the annual rainfall in less than an hour. Where vegetation exists, it is low and sparse and there is a notable lack of shade.

Temperatures may range from well below freezing to over 130° F. And over what to some is a miserable and desolate scene, and to others is sheer bliss, often blows a strong desiccating wind. Obviously merely to stay alive in such an environment takes a splendid adaptation.

Not All Cacti Grow in Deserts

SOME CACTI GROW in grasslands and some bordering the sea, while others grow in the steaming tropical jungles of Mexico and South America. Of these latter there are those that prefer the open sunshine and others nearby that prefer to live up in shady trees, in the manner of orchids, and from whose long fleshy branches drops of moisture fall.

(bottom left)
We usually associate cacti with deserts, but there is as much variety in their habitats as in their shapes. This *Lobivis aurea* with its golden flower comes from the high Andes of South America. Other cacti prefer grasslands, seacoasts and even tropical jungles.

(bottom right)
Since most trees lose water through their leaves, the leafless cacti can hold water more easily than other plants. However, they still need protection from the hot sun, and some shade is provided by their **numerous spines,** which break up the sunshine and may even reflect it. The spines also keep hungry and thirsty animals away.

Heat, low humidity and less than twelve inches of annual rainfall are common desert conditions. Those plants that can survive in such an environment, like these cacti in the **Arizona desert,** must be well-adapted. In general desert vegetation is sparse, and it is rarely as tall as these cacti, especially in deserts in other parts of the world.

There is as much variety in the conditions in which they like to live as there is in their shapes. Many can only survive in the full glare of the hot sun; others happily tolerate the cold snowy winters of the high Andes. Many need a rich loamy soil with plenty of moisture at least during their growing period, others are content with the poorest and driest of conditions such as rocky mountain slopes. But wherever they are found, there is one thing that not one of them can endure for long, and that is to have their roots sitting in poorly-drained soil.

Though geographically they are to be found from Massachusetts in the United States down to the Straits of Magellan, Mexico can be considered to be their classical home. There they flourish in the greatest numbers and the greatest variety.

How Desert Cactus Lives

IF ONE COULD IMAGINE converting oneself into a plant that had to exist in the desert, one outstanding problem would immediately come to mind—that of water. Almost before our head was above the ground, we would have had to figure out how to get water and how to store it once we had absorbed it.

First we would develop a wide-spreading root system lying but a

(above)
Many plants of arid regions have **bulblike underground roots** that are apparently used to store food. Some may weigh as much as 125 pounds.

(above, right)
The constant and vital search for water forces desert plants to develop an efficient root system in order to survive. The **saguaro's roots** must spread widely in all directions; hence the plants are not found close together.

few inches beneath the surface of the ground. In this way as much of the surface moisture as possible could be absorbed before it evaporated or penetrated deeper. The saguaro root radius often equals the height of the plant itself and after a heavy rain it is able to carry hundreds of gallons of water to the stem.

Then we would develop a thick fleshy loosely constructed body that could expand in the times of plenty. Again the accordion-pleated saguaro is a good example. During droughts its body slowly contracts as the water within is used, the grooves or pleats thus becoming more and more pronounced. After a good rain it swells so that its surface is a great deal smoother.

Not only do we have to contrive to store as much water as possible, but we must endeavor to lose as little as possible of what we have successfully stored away. A large tree may lose several hundred gallons a day through moisture transpiring or evaporating from the pores in its leaves, much as the human skin loses moisture through perspiration. For a desert dweller this obviously wouldn't do at all. So to inhibit such a waste we would do away with leaves and coat our trunk and branches with perhaps a waterproof waxlike substance. We are growing to look more and more like a cereus every minute.

Other Problems to Survival

YET WE HAVE JUST MADE a beginning. Bare trunk and branches, unprotected by leaves from the hot drying wind and the merciless sun, would soon be scorched. Therefore along with abandoning our leaves, we would develop spines. Cacti thrive in broken sunshine, especially when they are young and tender. Many who have grown these plants know that the lath-house affords them welcome protection against day after day of unbroken rays of sunshine. Look at the shadows thrown by the spines and the slat-house effect is plainly noticeable. If they were sufficiently abundant, as in the teddy bear cholla, they might even reflect the sun. So the spines would provide the necessary amount of shade and also act as something of a windbreak. Equally important, they would provide protection from hungry and thirsty animals that might fancy our juicy stems for dinner, as well as from mealbound snails and slugs.

Yet without leaves we run the risk of starving to death, for we have thus eliminated our food factories. So to carry on the vital process of photosynthesis, we would have to set up new cell factories in our trunk and branches, which would then turn green due to the necessary presence of chlorophyll.

No longer are our stems merely canals to be used only for the transportation of liquids and food to and from the leaves, or as devices for holding out the leaves to the sun. Now they have become self-sufficient food producers as well as water reservoirs.

Tricks to Be Learned

ANOTHER TRICK WE MIGHT LEARN is that of going into a state of dormancy when things get difficult, as during an extended drought. Some deserts may go for years without rain and the cacti that manage to stay alive have learned to sleep it out. This, along with the inevitably shortened rations due to leaf loss, cuts down on the growth rate, but rapid growth is a luxury which those that live in the desert cannot afford, any more than they can afford green leaves.

Our shape, too, would be important, for we would want to combine the minimum surface from which to lose water with the maximum internal space in which to store it. Ideally, then, we would end up being cylindrical like a barrel cactus or a saguaro—not a thing of beauty, perhaps, but eminently practical.

Spines Aid in Propagation

MOST CACTI PROPAGATE in the regular manner by producing flowers which in due course turn into fruit with seeds, but a few propagate from the joints of the plant itself. The jumping cholla produces long chains of fruit which become increasingly heavy and finally break

(above)
Cacti grow in a variety of conditions, including those of high mountainous areas. This cactus, found south of La Paz, Bolivia, is one of the many examples of **cacti that grow at high altitudes.**

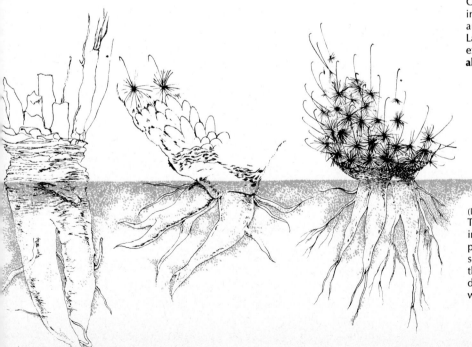

(left)
The **roots of cacti** are sometimes immense compared to the size of the plants. Roots that are close to the surface can absorb moisture from even the lightest rain, while those that dig deep into the ground may tap the water table.

off and take root. For this reason they are also sometimes called the chain fruit cactus.

Cactus spines are a further source of help in the propagation and distribution of the species. Whenever a terminal stem catches on to a passerby and is broken off, there is the possibility of its being carried some distance away. When it at last is dropped to the ground it can take root and eventually produce a new plant.

A small insignificant type of opuntia has been widely distributed over the grassy plains of mid-western United States because its terminal joints break off so easily and become scattered. For this reason it has earned for itself the name of *Opuntia fragilis*. It is considered to be a pest in grazing country where it proves very troublesome to the range animals.

Insects play their traditional role in the propagation of cacti, along with other plants, by spreading their pollen. Many cerei blossoms open at night and hence are fertilized primarily by night-flying insects. In this connection it is interesting to note that the nectar-feeding bat helps to propagate the saguaro as it feeds at the flowers.

Birds Defy the Spines

CACTUS WRENS, thrashers and finches, to name a few, build their nests in the prickly cholla, flying straight into them in an alarming fashion without suffering so much as a scratch. When one walks in the desert in the evening one is often startled by a wren suddenly flying out of a nearby cholla. Mammals, too, find shelter behind their prickles. Pack rats pile up cholla segments, sometimes within the confines of a sprawling prickly pear, to fortify their homes. Despite their soft bare hands and feet and tender mouths they carry these spiny objects about and scurry among them so heedlessly that to us it seems sheer folly, if not downright suicide.

Yet sometimes the incredible array of armament is not as much protection as one might suppose, for snakes and lizards often see cacti as a happy hunting ground, much to the disapproval of the residents. Anyone who has heard the loud harsh scolding of an angry cactus wren knows just how much the intruder is resented. Odd as it may sound, this particular alarm can be music to the ears of the naturalist out looking for a certain specimen, as it well may be an indication that a snake is nearby, and it may turn out to be the one he is after, in which case the hunter suddenly becomes the hunted.

Saguaros Take the Place of Trees

IN A LAND where trees are scarce, saguaros often serve as substitutes. A hawk may choose to build its nest in the notch of a branching arm and woodpeckers drill their cavities in the soft flesh. The cactus

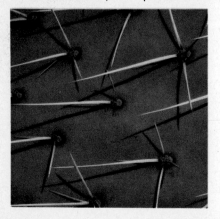

Spines are a deterrent to hungry and thirsty animals attracted by the juicy pads of a cactus. They may also provide **broken sunshine,** as this picture shows.

A **cylindrical shape** combines maximum storage room for holding water with minimum exposed area for surface evaporation. This is ideal for desert conditions such as those in this California setting.

then lines these holes with "scar tissue" which hardens into a sort of shoe, as it is popularly called. When the woodpecker moves out, an elf owl or some other bird moves in.

More than one bobcat has been known to climb to the top of a

**CHOLLA
3 TO 15 FEET**

saguaro when danger threatened, there being nothing else at hand. Those who saw Walt Disney's motion picture on the desert will recall the incredible sight of a bobcat being chased by peccaries or wild pigs and making a dash to the top of one of these huge cacti.

Other plants may also use the saguaro as a home. Occasionally one sees a prickly pear, for example, whose seed has been carried up to a fork by the wind or by an animal, growing high above the ground in a most unlikely fashion.

Cacti as a Source of Food

BESIDES PROVIDING PROTECTION, cacti are considered by many animals to be a very tasty meal. Rodents delight in gnawing away at prickly pear pads, and sometimes hardpressed cattle will develop a liking for cholla which they will eat, spines and all.

Insects, too, find the flesh of cacti very much to their taste. One of these is the robust cactus joint bug which, besides eating the cactus, lays its eggs in rows of from twelve to fifteen along the spines. This nocturnal creature often congregates in great numbers on cacti joints, eventually causing the death of the plant. The larvae of the Mexican cactus fly scavenge the decaying cactus, a worthwhile occupation indeed, while the cactus fruit gall fly confines its activities for the most part to the green and ripening fruit of the opuntia. Some members of this clan are said to form galls that greatly resemble the cactus fruit they are in the process of eating.

**SAGUARO
UP TO 60 FEET**

Saguaros take 25 years to reach a height of two feet, but when fully grown they may be up to 60 feet tall, which makes them the "trees" of the desert. Three to fifteen feet is more usual for the cholla.

SAGUARO CHOLLA PRICKLY PEAR NIGHT-BLOOMING CEREUS PINCUSHION

It is far easier for us to imagine the fruit being eaten than the prickly stems, even though they too are often covered with small clumps of minute barbed bristles. The yellow barrel cactus fruit are eaten by deer as well as rodents and it is a common sight in the Arizona desert to see a scattering of half-eaten fruit around the entrance to a ground squirrel's hole. The ripe fruit of the Brazilian pereskia, a most uncactus-like plant with leaves, is seldom found whole because as soon as the fruits begin to ripen birds peck into them for their large black seeds. The seeds from the saguaro fruit are considered a delicacy by the white-winged doves that feed on them predominantly when they are available.

The Saguaro—a Boon to the Papago Indians

THE SAGUARO has contributed greatly towards the subsistence of the Papago Indians of the American South-west. Its woodlike ribs provide material for the building of their rounded dwellings. Because of this plant's capacity for water storage and its slow growth rate, it is able to put forth fruit annually more or less regardless of drought and is therefore a dependable source of food. The fruit matures in early summer, providing a veritable feast for the Indians. Besides eating it fresh they make it into syrup and preserves. From the seeds they make a kind of butter and an intoxicating beverage is made from the juice which has been allowed to ferment.

(above)
Spines of the various cacti differ greatly. Some are fine and hairlike, others short and thorny, and some are long, slender needles.

(below, left)
Shape and size vary as widely among cacti as they do within any group of plants. Prickly pear, two to four feet tall, is remarkably unlike the night-blooming cereus or the relatively small pincushion.

(below)
The **cane cholla** belongs to the same genus as the prickly pear. After first removing the spines by burning, ranchers sometimes use this cactus as fodder for their cattle.

**PRICKLY PEAR
2-4 FEET**

**NIGHT-BLOOMING
CEREUS
1-2 FEET**

**PINCUSHION
2-10 INCHES**

The fruit of the organ pipe cactus is also eaten by the Indians, as well as that of the prickly pear. The huge tubers of the night-blooming cereus are sliced and fried in fat, while the young joints of the pencil cholla are boiled and served as a vegetable. Further south the Yaqui Indians use the seeds of their saguaro-like cactus, the cardon, by grinding them into a flour to make tamales.

In South America a kind of prickly pear is cultivated by the natives for its seeds, which are gathered, dried and sold in the markets as "ayrampo". The seeds, when put in water, yield a red substance used to color jellies and gelatines. This coloring actually comes from the red juice of the fruit which has dried on the exterior of the seed rather than from the seed itself. Wherever Indians live, cacti have been used by them in a variety of ways, but especially as a source of building materials and food.

Cochineal Dye—an Ancient Industry

A TALL TREELIKE CACTUS, *Nopalea cochenillifera*, that looks something like a prickly pear, earned its specific name because of the part it and related species played in the production of the once famous cochineal dye. At first cochineal was thought to be a product of the plant itself, but later it was discovered that in reality the source of the dye was a scale insect that lived on the plant. The female secretes a white waxlike substance for protection as it goes about the business of feeding on the juicy flesh of the cacti. These creatures become so numerous that the surface of the plant appears to be white.

The cochineal industry goes back into prehistory, for the Spaniards found it already well established in Mexico at the time of their arrival

(bottom left)
The female scale insect secretes a white waxlike substance for protection as it feeds on the flesh of this cactus. This is used in the making of the famous **cochineal dye,** an industry that goes back to pre-Columbian Mexico.

(bottom right)
This **barrel cactus** is very conspicuous in the Sonoran Desert of southern Arizona. Because of its southward lean, which may serve as a directional guide to travelers, the barrel cactus is also called the "compass cactus." Species may be found ranging from a few inches to as much as eleven feet in height.

(left)
The **prickly pear,** which has spread to much of the world, bears fruit that is eaten by man as well as by animals. The tender young pads may also be eaten after they have been cooked and their spines are removed.

(above)
A tiny plant known as the **claret-cup cactus** produces this beautiful red flower. The cactus itself is variable both as to habitat and as to the number of its spines.

in the beginning of the sixteenth century. They began to export the product, which was soon in such demand throughout Europe that it became a favorite form of tribute to the Spanish Crown. The plant itself was also introduced into Europe and soon great plantations were under cultivation. In one year, in the 1860's, over six million pounds of this dye, valued at four million dollars, were exported from the Canary Islands alone.

The insects were put on the cactus joints where they quickly multiplied. Two or three times a year they were brushed off into containers and then dried in a number of ways to make the dye. While the colors were brilliant, they were not very permanent. With the development of aniline dyes the cochineal industry has just about disappeared, though they are still used in the coloring of cosmetics.

The Famous Peyote

IN RECENT YEARS much has been said about the hallucination-producing cactus, *Lophophora Williamsii,* used by various Indians since pre-Columbian times in certain kinds of ceremonies. This small modest plant, popularly called peyote, is found in the deserts from central Mexico to southern Texas.

The plant is a dull bluish green, very succulent, and looks somewhat like a child's top, or perhaps even a spineless sea urchin. Only as a seedling does it have spines and these are weak and insignificant bristles. It also has a fairly long thickened tap-root, rather rare in cacti that on the whole prefer a shallow root system.

Scientists have been busily studying the chemical, medicinal and therapeutic properties of this curious plant. At first it was thought that the active drug contained in the cactus lay in the alkaloids, but later certain resinous bodies were thought to be responsible. Scientists have also been studying the psychological effects which follow the eating of dried pieces of the plant. It is said to sometimes make the unaccustomed eater sick to his stomach, but apparently the remarkable and intense

In Mexico a suitable cactus is often handy as a hayrack, as this picture of a **cereus** illustrates. It was found growing a few miles south of Guanajuato, Mexico. This is just one of the many uses that man has found for members of the cactus family.

visions that result are a sufficient reward. During these one's perceptions are said to be so heightened that an ordinary object takes on incredible beauty and significance.

In Mexico, the stems of the cactus were topped and the tops dried and strung on a string like beads and then sold in the markets. A sixteenth-century Spaniard described its use by the Indians and, thinking it to be a fungus, named it teonanactl or sacred mushroom. It is also known as mescal button, devil's root and dumpling cactus. It is against the law to grow or possess it.

Modern Man Also Uses Cacti

THE CLASSIC VERSION of how a cactus can best serve man depicts the traveler dying of thirst on the desert. First you see him struggling along in the blazing sun and next you see him chopping open a barrel

With their beautiful, showy blossoms, it is no wonder that many cacti are used for decorative purposes in home and garden. Members of this tropical group, often called **orchid cacti,** are especially prized for their spectacular blooms in vivid colors.

The **hedgehog cactus** in the foreground is common on the Sonoran Desert. In the early spring it is topped with vivid blossoms.

cactus because therein he knows that he will find a refreshing liquid. This is not altogether the way it works. First of all, because of the stout interlacing spines, it is very difficult to cut into this plant with anything smaller than a machete. Secondly, when you finally do succeed in reaching the plant's interior, what you will find is a juicy pulp from which moisture can be extracted either by chewing, squeezing, or pounding. This is in some degree true of many cacti, but the flesh of the barrel cactus has the reputation of being the most suitable.

The barrel cactus has further gained fame as the traveler's aid by serving as a directional signpost. Because of this it is also called the compass cactus. Anyone who has seen it growing will have noticed that it has a decidedly southward lean to it. Therefore it is just as helpful in the daytime in its way as the North Star is during the night.

Much more acceptable to the palate than the flesh of cacti are its fruits, which are relished by many. In the West Indies the fruit of one of the pereskias is considered a great delicacy and is called the Barbados gooseberry, though it is also known as the blade apple. In Brazil the leaves are used as a pot herb. The fruit of some of the prickly pear, known as tuna fruit, is also prized and sold extensively in Latin American markets. The tender young pads are eaten after having been rid of their spines, cut into strips, and roasted, boiled or fried.

Popular Cactus Products

EXAMPLES OF THE USES OF CACTI are usually abundant in south-western United States novelty shops that cater to tourists. One can find jars of cactus jam and jelly and boxes of cactus candy, as well as a variety of objects made out of the bare dried skeletons of the

Prickly pear is the most widely distributed cactus in the world, having been introduced nearly everywhere by man; in Australia it spread over 10 million acres in little more than fifty years. Some varieties grow to several feet in height, while others are low-growing. The roots are fibrous and shallow, extending outwards in their attempt to trap what little water is available.

(top)
One of the handsomest of the barrel cacti, **golden barrel cactus** is much prized by collectors. Its blossoms open during the day and close as soon as the sunlight leaves the flower.

(above)
These showy white flowers belong to the familiar **night-blooming cereus** of the Sonoran Desert. A most uncharacteristic-looking cactus, the plant can best be described as a scraggily bunch of seemingly dead sticks.

plants themselves. Especially suited to this are the lattice-like skeletons of the cholla, which can be found lying about on the desert. These are made into lamp bases, picture frames and other novelty items. Also available are cellophane-wrapped boxes containing small samples of living specimens to be taken home and planted in pots.

In this connection there is a story about a lady who was successfully growing Arizona pincushions in her New York City apartment. On being asked how she knew when to water them, she replied that she subscribed to an Arizona newspaper and whenever it reported rain she watered her cacti. This story further serves to illustrate the fact that more and more people throughout the world are growing cacti as a hobby, whether in pots or in their gardens. The hybrid epiphyllums, often called orchid cacti, are particularly popular because of their spectacular blooms in vivid colors, up to nine inches in diameter.

Cacti are also used medicinally. In Mexico the rat-tail cactus is grown in the end of a cow's horn and the dried flowers, called Flor de Cuerno or horn-flowers, are a popular household remedy. And a kind of opuntia is used for the treatment of burns, as a laxative, and in the treatment of diabetes.

Cacti on the Ranch or Farm

MANY RANCHERS, during a period of drought when the range grass is scarce, will feed certain kinds of opuntia to their hungry cattle after first removing the spines by burning. The nearly spineless prickly pear that grows in tropical and sub-tropical countries is held in particular esteem as cattle fodder and can be considered of economic importance.

Where the right kind of cacti occur, they are planted as hedges to protect gardens and yards or even as windbreaks, for they form an impenetrable barrier. The ribs of the saguaro are used to make decorative fences and in many an old ranch house they add immeasurably to the beauty of a room by having been used in the construction of the ceiling. One of the most unusual sights in Mexico is that of a large many-branched cereus serving as a hayrack.

A less orthodox use of cholla segments than as cattle food, but a very effective one, is in flower beds to discourage dogs from digging, burying bones or napping in them. In the same way cholla joints are useful in keeping the family pets and small children out of potted plants, and it is remarkable what they can accomplish scattered along the top of a patio wall.

Some Important Arizona Cacti

THE FOUR MOST CONSPICUOUS TYPES of cacti which the visitor to the Sonoran Desert in southern Arizona will notice are the saguaro, the cholla, the prickly pear and the barrel cactus. Plant life in this arid land is surprisingly abundant and yet it is sparse enough to make walking easy.

The impression frequently given, especially where the desert is rather level, is that of a great botanical park, for the giant cacti and their numerous associates are often so spaced that progress from one interesting group to another offers no obstacles whatever. An exception will be found in some of the great stands of chollas. In some places, on the other hand, it does not seem possible that the planting was natural and one almost expects to see neat botanical labels on the plants giving their scientific names and ranges. Even in the mountains, in places where the going is rocky and rough, there is a decided spacing of the plant life that is impressive.

Prickly Pear Is Short-lived

N<small>EXT TO THE GIANT SAGUARO</small> the most familiar and easily recognized cactus in the south-western desert is the big flat-stemmed prickly pear. In contrast to the long-lived saguaro it seldom lives more than twenty years.

It belongs to the genus *Opuntia* (Tribe *Opuntieae*) and, due to man, it is the most widely distributed cactus in the world. It can be seen growing in Greek villages, South American towns and even in New England. In fact it sometimes grows too well; in Australia, where it was introduced, it spread from a flowerpot to cover 10 million acres of land in hardly more than fifty years. Through great effort and expense it was finally brought under control.

Valued by many for its edible fruit, **prickly pear** may be found growing from New England to northern South America. Many of the species possess long spines, but others have small, barbed bristles that are less easily noticed. Spines are modified leaves—they should not be confused with thorns (modified stems) or prickles. In the top picture, a prickly pear bloom attracts a bee; above, the most common cactus of the southwestern United States, a species of prickly pear bursts with bright yellow flowers.

Engelmann's prickly pear, *O. Engelmannii,* common in Arizona, may spread out as much as nine or ten feet with a height of four feet. The plants are made up of a few or perhaps hundreds of flat fleshy "leaves" or pads covered with long spines.

Similar, but less common, is the beavertail cactus, *O. basilaris.* It is also flat-stemmed, like the Engelmann's, but the stems are studded with little groups of minute and extremely irritating barbed bristles, or glochids, as they are technically called. These brush off and into a person's skin at the slightest touch, very much like nettle hairs. The small raised spots on the beavertail, replacing the obvious large spines of Engelmann's prickly pear, look very innocent, but each of these protuberances is made up of large numbers of microscopic crescent-shaped and thoroughly barbed bristles. This cactus seldom grows more than one foot high and its pads are often a handsome velvety grey.

The flowers of the Engelmann's prickly pear are a bright clear yellow and about three inches across. Those of the beavertail are smaller and typically a brilliant magenta or purple. Late in the summer the leaves of the Engelmann's prickly pear are studded with large handsome red fruit.

Other species of prickly pear bear such descriptive names as cow's

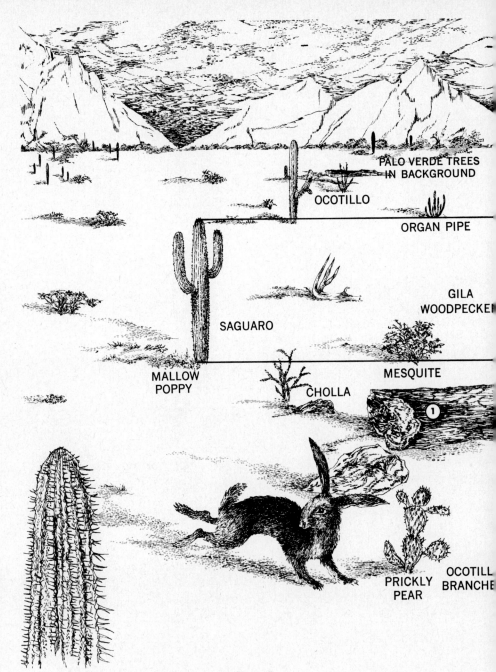

PALO VERDE TREES
IN BACKGROUND

OCOTILLO

ORGAN PIPE

GILA
WOODPECKE[R]

SAGUARO

MALLOW
POPPY

CHOLLA

MESQUITE

1

PRICKLY
PEAR

OCOTILL[O]
BRANCHE[S]

The two halves of this picture depict the changes in a desert scene after a period of fifty years, showing the amount of growth that has occurred. Unchanged, of course, is the petrified log (1), which is already 200 million years old. In general, the various plants have grown slowly; the saguaros, for example, have not even tripled in size. Cacti and shrubs space themselves at least five to ten feet apart, but mallow poppy grows close against the saguaro trunk.

tongue, rabbit's ear, pancake and grizzly bear, as well as the purple prickly pear whose leaves actually do turn purplish.

Chollas Are Also Opuntias

THE CHOLLAS, though very different looking from the prickly pear, belong to the same large genus *Opuntia*. Their stems are also jointed, but they are cylindrical or sausage-like without the flat paddle

Belonging to the same genus, *Opuntia*, as does the prickly pear, the **cholla** is usually around five or six feet tall, although it may grow much higher. It has jointed stems that are cylindrical in shape, unlike the flattened pads of the prickly pear. Cholla blossoms are of many colors.

CREOSOTE

appearance of the prickly pear. From a distance they look somewhat like a compact stubby shrub.

Some of the tree chollas grow to be over twelve feet tall, while others may be very small indeed. The pencil cholla, *O. arbuscula,* has stems no thicker than a pencil, hence its name. One of these delicately stemmed plants, called the Christmas cactus, *O. leptocaulis,* particularly brightens the Arizona desert in fall and winter with its small scarlet fruit.

One of the tree chollas is called the staghorn, because it branches in such a way as to suggest the antlers of deer. It may grow to twelve feet in height though usually it is not as tall as that. Its branches are numerous, measuring about an inch or so in diameter, and many are tinged with purple or red, while others are green or purplish green. The staghorn cholla is easily distinguished from the heavily-armed jumping chollas because its stems are thinner and its spines are shorter and sparser. The blossoms of the staghorn are spectacular in their variety and for that reason it has earned for itself the scientific name of *O. versicolor*. A short stroll through the desert in late spring will disclose blossoms in red, yellow, orange, chartreuse, rust, pink, fuchsia and purple. The Pima Indians use the flower buds of some of the tree chollas for food. They steam them in such a way that they keep for a time and can be eaten as needed, sometimes with saltbush greens.

The Jumping Cholla that Doesn't Jump

ONE OF THE MOST CHARACTERISTIC cacti of the Sonoran Desert is the tall chain fruit cactus, locally called jumping cholla or jumping cactus, *O. fulgida*. The visitor to the South-west will see these plants growing singly or in dense patches, according to locality. The grotesque forms of these desert inhabitants are crowned with bristling masses of extremely spiny, greenish-yellow branches, beneath which dangle long chains of sour fruit considered inedible by humans though grazing animals seem to eat them with placid enjoyment. There may be as many as forty or fifty fruits in a single cluster. The height of this cactus is usually around five or six feet, though they can grow to be much larger.

A human being cannot so much as touch one of them without becoming very painfully involved, since the spiny joints are so loosely attached that they seem to spring upon one if one passes too closely.

Smaller, much more compact and also bristling with spiny armament, is the teddy bear cholla, *O. Bigelovii*. It also is called jumping cholla, since it too has the same regrettable habit of fastening itself onto you if you happen to brush by. How such a plant could ever win for itself the name of teddy bear must seem ludicrous to the newcomer. But when seen from afar in a soft light these plants do have a nice soft fuzzy look like large cuddly teddy bears. They are exceedingly handsome for a cholla, with their contrasting black trunks and strawlike spines that catch the sunlight, particularly when back-lit in the late afternoon. Then they seem actually to glow.

Opuntias in Unlikely Places

THE FIRST THING that well may greet a voyager as he takes his first step onto the rocky shore of a Galápagos island is a prickly

Because its branches suggest the antlers of a deer, this tree cholla is popularly called the **staghorn cactus**. Its blossoms come in a spectacular variety of colors.

(left)
A **prickly pear tree**—a tree form of the tough prickly pear cactus—is found in some of the barrenest areas of the Galápagos Islands. The original seeds may have been dropped on these volcanic islands by birds, or they may have floated there on piles of debris.

(below)
These **pincushion cacti** may be found as single plants, but they often grow in clumps. Light-colored spines cover each rounded body, which can be measured in inches rather than feet. Pincushions belong to the group known as *Mammillaria*.

pear tree, *O. galapageia*. If he is singularly lucky it will be a tall one, perhaps thirty feet high, with a rough reddish bark like that of a pine.

The perceptive traveler, appreciating the difficulty of reaching these remote volcanic islands located about 150 miles off the coast of Ecuador, may next ask himself how in the world these plants ever managed to get there when he barely did. Some of the seeds may have been dropped onto these shores by birds newly arrived from the mainland, others may have floated there on piles of debris swept down a mainland river and further propelled by wind and current.

Next the traveler would ask himself why these cacti are so much bigger than their cousins on the mainland. Gigantism is one of the peculiarities often present in the flora and fauna of oceanic islands, as for example the huge tortoises that inhabit the Seychelles as well as the Galápagos.

High in the Andes, at an altitude of from ten to fifteen thousand feet, grows another kind of opuntia, *O. floccosa*. It grows in clumps or low mounds that may spread out to six feet, with hundreds of short branches. It is a singular plant not only because of its location but because of its appearance, for from a distance it can easily be mistaken for just another patch of snow. This is due to the cactus being thickly covered with long white silky "hairs" which hide the sharp spines within. "The unwary stranger," wrote a naturalist on seeing them, "who should be tempted to use these wooly mounds for a seat would suffer from the experiment." This plant has also been described as a small white shaggy sheep dog, or as a caricature of an arctic creature.

The Towering Saguaros

OF THE MANY KINDS OF CEREI growing in Arizona, the one that most dominates the scene wherever it occurs is the giant saguaro,

The fruit of many cacti, such as this species of *Gymnocalycium*, are fancied by many people, provided the animals haven't gotten to the fruit first. Spine-inflicted injuries are the main hazards in harvesting. In this genus, the spines spread and recurve, and in one species this is so pronounced that the plant resembles a spider.

Carnegiea gigantea. There is nothing else like these tall green columns in this area.

The saguaro, a resident of the Sonoran Desert, also occurs in the state of Sonora, in Mexico. Its habitat is from near sea level up to some four thousand feet on the flanks of the mountains. Saguaros may grow to nearly fifty feet in height, although most of them are not nearly so tall. Their trunks and branches are thick and accordion-pleated and the branches may grow out in all sorts of ways, some growing downward and then turning up towards the sky again. They may have as many as fifty arms, or just one sticking out like a bulbous nose halfway up, or none at all.

As large as the saguaro is, however, it is not as tall as the Argentinian cereus, *Cereus dayamii,* which grows to be over eighty feet high. Its flowers are also larger, growing up to ten inches in length, and it has edible fruit as has the saguaro but with white pulp instead of red.

Saguaros Have No Growth Rings

GAZING UPON A THICK HEAVY SAGUARO trunk, one realizes that these cacti are trees of a sort, yet if one cuts into it with a knife the going will be easy, as if one were scooping out the rind of an unripe melon. If one slices a saguaro in half, the first thing that will be evident is that there are no growth rings. Instead, imbedded in the pale flesh, there are round woodlike rods growing in a circle about halfway out from the center. These act as a supporting frame and increase in thickness as the plant ages.

The saguaros' tough outer hide is impervious to sun and wind that might otherwise rob them of the moisture so carefully gathered and

Outlined against an Arizona sunset, this tall **saguaro** overshadows the desert landscape. It is difficult to believe that, botanically, saguaros are closely allied to violets, oleasters and passion flowers.

stored in their accordion-pleated stems. Their perpendicular ribs of tissue may expand and contract accommodatingly as moisture is husbanded or expended, yet at all times they seem capable of retaining the necessary percentage of water of which a healthy cactus body is composed. They have evolved tremendously efficient though shallow root systems in order to gather the required moisture, and the tentacles of these systems reach out in many directions under the desert sand. In other words, they are exceedingly well adapted to such a rigorous climate.

They Grow Slowly and Live Long

A SAGUARO MAY WEIGH as much as ten tons, most of which is water. That this bulk is due chiefly to stored up water sucked up from the desert dawns upon the visitor only gradually, but the great age of some of them is suggested at once by their size. Scientists are reluctant to state the age of these cacti, but the largest may well be over 200 years old. Their growth is very slow, requiring ten years to grow the first inch. Larger plants may grow three or four inches in a year, or more in wet years.

Shortly after a heavy rain a saguaro may increase its girth an inch or more. Should a saguaro be within reach of your garden hose you can conduct this experiment for yourself and you will notice, after a week or more of persistent watering, that it will be remarkably fatter. Saguaros and other cacti may live for long periods when uprooted altogether and left lying around in the dry atmosphere of the desert, which is another proof of how much water they contain.

The Saguaro Blossom Is the Arizona State Flower

IT SEEMS ALTOGETHER APPROPRIATE that the saguaro blossom is the Arizona state flower. Not only does it appear on the state's largest cactus, but the flower itself is worthy of such an honor. Though these have no fragrance in the usual meaning of the word, they have an odor like that of ripe melon, which to some may be infinitely more appealing than the traditional sweetness of a flower.

In April or May, after the winter rains have come and gone, and after stoic periods of waiting that would easily defeat a less rugged plant, the saguaro suddenly awakens into action by quickly pushing forth its buds into gorgeously expanding blossoms. The buds are about five inches long and appear as though encased in narrow rounded green shingles. The beautiful white or greenish-white flower petals are like wax, while the large number of small pale yellow stamens in the flower's throat look rather like fur.

The student of desert plants will often be astonished at the rapidity with which they accomplish their blossoming and fruiting once they start. In June or July the egg-shaped fruit has formed and ripened;

Woodlike rods that grow thicker as the plant increases in size provide a supporting frame for the **saguaro.** When the cactus dies, these rods form a skeleton that may stand upright for years. Through the parched ages the tall cacti have learned the secret of long life, but a bacterial infection spread by a disease-bearing moth has brought destruction to many of these giants.

these soon split open, the sections curling back and revealing the red pulp studded with hundreds of small black seeds. Large numbers of these seeds must mature each year and it would seem that, despite their many natural enemies, enough of them would find sanctuary in the sand and rocks to dot the land later with saguaro offspring. Unfortunately this is not so. Very rarely can one find recently born seedlings or even young plants. The old ones, however, are present in vast numbers in many areas and the visitor will find endless delight in discovering new and curiously formed specimens. In certain areas, around Tucson, Arizona, for instance, they grow close enough together so as to suggest a forest, though a very extraordinary forest indeed, with little shade and no soft rustling leaves.

Few Young Saguaros

IT IS A STARTLING FACT that over all the cactus lands the visitor will discover few young saguaros. Those present are well concealed and they also seem to have been reduced in the past by the introduction of domestic stock animals. These beasts, in their search for food, trampled and destroyed the natural cover which the young cacti demand, while many of the small desert rodents eat the newly germinated ones, unchecked as they are by the absence of coyotes.

The early settlers waged a relentless war upon the coyotes, the desert foxes and the other natural enemies of the rodents. They still often do this in a most thoughtless manner, and coyotes are shot at the minute they appear. These large canines harmed the settlers' stock, it is true, but the coyote in particular constituted a very important check upon the abundant kangaroo and wood rats, the swarming ground squirrels and pocket mice, the jack rabbits and the others which forthwith began to increase in proportion as their enemies were reduced or eliminated. Then, as now, these rodent armies attacked the cacti and their seeds, and consumed them when the plants were very young. They carried off the saguaro seeds and devoured them. Those seeds, ejected in excrement by birds which ate them in cactus fruit, were doubtless gathered up a second time by still other hungry creatures, for little or nothing which is edible goes to waste in the desert.

When man steps into the picture he often upsets the delicate balance of desert life which has existed successfully for so long before his arrival and which has been set up by nature in her wonderful and painstaking manner. The settlers and the present-day stock raisers cannot be altogether blamed for killing some coyotes, but certainly not all of the coyotes should be eliminated.

Not as Healthy as They Look

AT FIRST SIGHT the desert cactus forests seem healthy and undisturbed. But when the visitor looks longer and more carefully he

Saguaros blossom in April or May, producing beautiful waxlike flowers with white or greenish-white petals. The blossoms open at night and have no fragrance. With dependable regularity—almost regardless of drought —the **saguaro flower turns into an edible red fruit** that ripens in early summer. The fruit may be eaten fresh or made into syrup and preserves, while a fermented beverage can be made from the juice and a type of butter from the seeds.

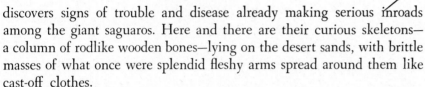

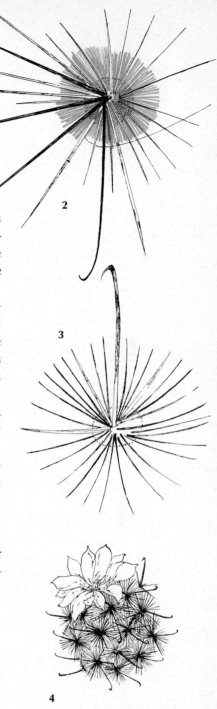

discovers signs of trouble and disease already making serious inroads among the giant saguaros. Here and there are their curious skeletons—a column of rodlike wooden bones—lying on the desert sands, with brittle masses of what once were splendid fleshy arms spread around them like cast-off clothes.

In some fortunate localities the disease is far less prevalent or noticeable than in others and many people who pass through as casual visitors hardly realize the presence of trouble at all. What will happen to the saguaros as time goes on no one can say for sure, but the trouble seems bound to spread where the saguaros grow close together or in groups as they often do.

They suffer from a bacterial infection. A disease-bearing moth lays its eggs within the cactus stem; the caterpillars that emerge bore their way through the plant tissue, carrying the infection with them; then when they transform, the adults fly off to other saguaros, thus transferring the disease and thereby bringing destruction to a magnificent gathering. Century-old giants now tumble in crumbling disarray.

In fact, in wandering among a cactus forest, the visitor will find much dead wood. Dead cholla limbs, after the living material has rotted away, look like silver-grey lacework, due to the silica and other mineral matter which the plant absorbed while alive. And saguaro skeletons, still upright, lend a strange note to an already strange scene.

The Cardon, a Saguaro-like Cactus

ALSO GROWING IN THE SONORAN DESERT, but farther to the south, is the cardon, *Pachycereus pringlei*. It and the saguaro, to which it bears a close resemblance, intermingle in north-western Mexico and, like the saguaro, it too dominates the landscape.

Another tree-type cereus of the Sonoran Desert is the organ pipe cactus, *Lemaireocereus Thurberi*. It grows twenty feet or more in height and its columnar branches, which are prominently ribbed but more slender than those of the cardon or saguaro, leave the main stem at or near ground level and rarely branch again unless injured. It is these numerous tall straight-rising branches that give the cactus its name. The flowers appear in the late spring, open at night, and vary from a

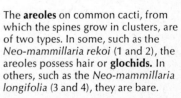

The **areoles** on common cacti, from which the spines grow in clusters, are of two types. In some, such as the *Neo-mammillaria rekoi* (1 and 2), the areoles possess hair or **glochids.** In others, such as the *Neo-mammillaria longifolia* (3 and 4), they are bare.

A desert seems little more than a sun-baked wasteland to most people. This scene of the varied birdlife of the southern Arizona desert, however, clearly shows the error of that notion. A pyrrhuloxia sings from a thorny perch above a covey of Gambel's quail (left margin), while a cactus wren rests a moment on a cactus pad. The roadrunner of cartoon fame stalks its prey beneath the pair of curve-billed thrashers that have nested in the large cactus at the right. The bright red cardinal coming in for a landing to the right of the pair of scaled quail resting in the sand is a stray, for it is very seldom found that far west.

greenish white to a brownish green, sometimes with bronzy tints in them. The Mexicans call its sweet fruit "pitahaya dulce", which means just that.

Growing along with the organ pipe cactus is an even denser clump cactus, *Lophocereus Schottii,* which may boast of as many as a hundred upright branches. Due to the long bristly spines which cover the ends of the flowering stems, this cactus is also locally called the old one, though this name more properly belongs to *Cephalocereus senilis* or the old man cactus. This latter cactus grows throughout Mexico and has long been considered a curiosity because the young plants are covered with long white beardlike "hairs". In fact at this stage in its growth it rather looks like a small version of Rip Van Winkle after his twenty-year sleep.

The Night-blooming Cereus Is a Cactus

ANOTHER CEREUS belonging to the same group as the saguaro and organ pipe, and one which will surprise the visitor to the Arizona desert when he first finds it, is the night-blooming cereus, *Peniocereus Greggii.* Appropriately called the Queen of the Night, its strange brittle sticklike stems grow unnoticed, usually in the shelter of some bush or tree.

The pink-tinged white flowers appear on one or two nights in late May or June. At dusk the buds open out into beautiful blossoms of four or five inches, fading the following day and withering into sad little masses—all so quickly after months of preparation. The easiest way to discover them is to smell them out during the night that they bloom. They have an exceedingly sweet odor very easy to detect that spreads out through the desert and transforms it into an Arabian Night.

(below)
The flowers of some cacti, including the saguaro and organ pipe cactus, blossom only at night and then fade and wither the following day. The large, pink-tinged, white flowers of the **night-blooming cereus** appear on one or two nights in late May or June, filling the air with their sweet fragrance.

(right)
Branches that leave the main stem near ground level and form a cluster of slender columns give this cactus its shape—and its name: the **organ pipe cactus.** A tree-type cereus found in the Sonoran Desert, it may exceed twenty feet in height and is night-blooming, flowering in the late spring.

The root of the night-blooming cereus consists of a long tuber that sometimes weighs as much as eighty pounds and is a dramatic contrast to the few fragile sticks that it nurtures. It functions most successfully as a storage place for food and water without which the scrawny plant could never live. The tuber is eaten by the Indians and, when ground up, is used as a poultice to ease chest congestions.

On the whole the night-blooming flowers are larger than diurnal ones and of these the moon cerei, *Selenicereus*, produce among the largest. In the tropics these climbing vines, which range from southern Texas through Mexico and Central America to the northern coast of South America, can reach to the tops of high trees, supported as they are by aerial roots. Flowers from eight to twelve inches long are common while some are as long as fifteen.

(above, left)
Commonly **barrel cacti** are two to four feet high, although they range in height from a few inches to more than ten feet. Many have stout, hooked spines that are reputed to be the worst ones to tangle with of any cactus. The blooms usually appear from April to September and vary from reds and pinks to oranges and yellows.

(above, right)
This unusual member of the *Cereae* tribe, the same group to which the huge saguaros belong, looks like a small agave. Thin, papery spines grow out of the ends of stiff, fleshy leaves, which are clustered together in a compact bunch.

The Conspicuous Barrel Cactus

THE BARREL CACTI are common in the cactus forest association of the Sonoran Desert where species may be found ranging from a few inches to as much as eleven feet in height, although most of them are about two to four feet high, with a diameter of from one to two feet. In Mexico they are reported to be up to six feet in diameter and to weigh several hundred pounds. Most are covered with hard, down-turned, fishhook-like spines which are surrounded by groups of straighter spines pointing in all directions. These spines vary in color from reddish to almost white. The barrel cactus enjoys the reputation of having the toughest, longest, broadest and meanest spines in the business. In fact its generic name comes from a word meaning wild or fierce.

In late summer the common barrel cacti of southern Arizona, *Ferocactus Wislenzii,* are crowned with lovely orange-red or yellow flowers which eventually turn into bright yellow fruit. These look something like tiny pineapples and if the birds and rodents have not found them first, they are filled with hard black seeds. Growing singly, or in clumps of hundreds of heads, as does *Ferocactus robustus,* the barrel cactus is a very handsome addition to the south-western flora.

One of the earliest cacti known to Europeans was the Turk's head cactus, *Melocactus,* whose body is very similar to that of the barrel. However its top does not, for it is surmounted by a roundish tuft of reddish bristles that looks rather like a brush with which to polish floors. In some species this tuft grows to be fourteen inches high and it sits on top of the cactus like some peculiar kind of hat.

The Cactus that's Named After the Hedgehog

KNOWN ALSO AS THE STRAWBERRY CACTUS, *Echinocereus,* because of the taste of its fruit, the hedgehog is common to the Sonoran Desert though perhaps it is not as often noticed as the larger more spectacular inhabitants. This cactus forms small clumps up to several feet in diameter, though one specimen has been recorded with five hundred stems. The stems, usually two to three inches in diameter, grow to a height of about one foot. They bristle with long sharp spines that may vary on one plant from black or brown to yellow, white or even translucent.

This rather insignificant cactus really comes into its own in the spring when it puts out two- to three-inch flowers in lovely reds, lavenders and purples, which decorate the desert with brilliant splashes of color. A plant at the University of Arizona in Tucson has had several hundred blooms open at one time.

Another member of this group to be seen growing in the Sonoran Desert is the rainbow cactus, *Echinocereus rigidissimus,* which gets its name from its brightly colored spines arranged in horizontal bands. One striking specimen has wide bands of red spines separated by narrow bands of white ones.

Danger! Fishhooks Present

LAST BUT NOT LEAST in attractiveness among the characteristic cacti of the Arizona desert are the tiny pincushion cacti which belong to the group known as *Mammillaria.* These may be found as single nubbins or in small groups, and are measured in inches rather than in feet. The rounded body of each plant is almost entirely hidden beneath delicate light-colored spines. In some species the longer spines are sharply hooked and catch the finger of the investigator with uncanny regularity. Appropriately, they are known as the fishhook cactus.

Growing in small clumps with stems about a foot high, the **hedgehog cactus** is also called the strawberry cactus because of the flavor of its fruit. In the spring its bright flowers, in shades of red and purple, attract a host of insects, which act as pollinators.

These cacti often can be found growing under bushes in rocky soil or in the open, high on ridges and surrounded with colorful rock fragments tinted with yellow, rust or green lichens. In March or April, they put forth a crown of little flowers with pink or lavender petals which last long enough to attract a host of small insect pollinators. These small cacti, especially in bloom, have all the charm of tiny things and are a delight to come upon in something as austere as the desert.

A close relative of the mammillarias is a cactus called the living rock, *Ariocarpus fissuratus,* in Texas. A dull brown or grey plant, it grows in dry stony ground and when not in flower can easily be mistaken for just another of the many surrounding rocks. It is very popular with collectors because of its imitative coloring. When one species of this genus was first discovered, three specimens were sent to Europe, of which one sold for around $200. As the plant probably weighed about half an ounce, it was then worth a good deal more than its weight in gold.

A Few More Notable Members of the *Cereae* Tribe

IN LOWER CALIFORNIA there grows a relative of such a mighty fellow as the saguaro that prefers to extend its length upon the ground rather than up into the air. Its generic name—*Machaerocereus*—means dagger cereus, referring to the quality of its spines, but one species is popularly called the creeping devil. And so, indeed, it appears to be. Its prostrate stems are from three to nine feet long with the growing end slightly uplifted as if it were looking around for something. As it lengthens the bottom side takes root and the back end slowly withers and dies so that it actually does move over the ground. When it comes to a low enough obstacle, such as a log or rock, it oozes up and over it, rerooting itself on the other side.

Crowned with flowers (top) or with bright red fruit (above), the **fishhook cactus** is an attractive sight. Delicate spines nearly hide the body of the cactus, while longer, sharply hooked spines—from which it gets its name—are a menace to both investigator and fruit-gatherer.

A mass of these things looks like something very sinister out of science fiction—perhaps a new kind of gigantic caterpillar. Though its fruits are edible, a fish poison is made by mashing the stems into a pulp which is then tossed into a stream.

Another peculiar member of this tribe found in parts of Mexico looks more like a small agave, *Leuchtenbergia principis.* It has thin papery spines growing from the truncated ends of the long grey-green fleshy leaves that grow in a stiff upright compact bunch. Also uncactus-like is its long taproot. It was named for Eugène de Bauharnais, Duke of Leuchtenberg and Prince of Eichstädt, a French soldier and statesman who was born in 1781.

And of course there is that whole queer group of epiphytic cacti belonging to the genus *Epiphyllum* that live in trees in tropical forests. Their stems look like narrow fleshy leaves and most of them are slightly scalloped. These plants are also known as the orchid cacti, not only because of where they grow but because of their large spectacular blossoms. These sprout from the stems as in other cacti, but because the

Besides beautiful flowers, this **barrel cactus** has the longest, toughest and meanest spines in the business. Its generic name comes from a word meaning wild or fierce.

stems look so much like leaves they give the flowering plant a strange appearance. Looking at them it is easy to see why their name comes from two Greek words meaning "upon" and "leaf".

The Desert Exudes Tranquillity

TRANQUILLITY OF A PROFOUND NATURE seems to pervade the scene in a cactus forest and it is this quality that most impresses itself on the visitor. As he becomes more familiar with the harsh nature of the desert, he will be increasingly astonished by the variety of life in what seems to be such an inhospitable place. For living things to have adapted themselves to such an environment in the beginning must have been very difficult at best; for them to live and propagate and continue successfully is no less difficult now. Each plant and animal is necessary to the success of the whole. Each has its role to play in maintaining the balance. Such balances are remarkable, but often little appreciated and understood, for although the living things evolved in ways which are in the end mutually beneficial, they often appear to be destroying one another rather than helping one another to survive. It is really this preying of one upon the other which preserves the balance so nicely.

Such balances may not be static, although many things in the cactus forest associations seem to have remained unchanged for ages and from now on they may show little or no further evolutionary progress. However, complexes may be altered and rebalanced successfully at times by nature, whereas if man steps in he may easily and permanently disturb them through his carelessly conceived controls or thoughtless extermination of one or more of the necessary species.

Every fruit and seed and flower is of importance, though we cannot always say why or how. It is a wonderful experience indeed to view at close range and at leisure the array of plant life which has evolved and flourished in the untouched arid regions. Small wonder that more and more people are becoming fascinated by the bizarre and highly diverse cacti which have shown such resourcefulness in their evolution.

▶ *A limited environment for living things but full of ingenious adaptations that make life possible.*

Dune Life

ON ALL THE CONTINENTS of the earth, sand dunes, whether coastal or far inland, give the impression of being barren of life. In fact to some people it might seem that life could exist only along the edges which border on more fertile territory. But actually the dune world is alive with specialized inhabitants which leave dainty tracks in the sand as they move about. The fact that these imprints are usually erased by the next gust of wind is immaterial. Momentarily they have told a story. And when the wind gains in strength, the dunes themselves become alive and go through constant changes in form. The only areas that remain the same for more than a day or so are those where vegetation has an anchoring effect or where wet, heavy sand resists the wind.

Dunes Behind the Beaches

TO MANY OF US dunes are most commonly associated with seashores. These dunes are the result of wave and wind action which throws up a large barrier dune at the back of the beach. This acts as a dike to waves and tide, and behind this dike there are often smaller dunes, caused by wind-carried sand being lifted over the barrier and allowed to settle in its lee. Sometimes a storm of hurricane strength will build and destroy dunes within a few hours. Anyone familiar with seashores knows how easily loose sand can shift and change during a season.

Dunes Far Inland

THERE ARE OTHER kinds of dunes, though, for every continent has sandy inland areas which are miniature deserts. These masses, often composed of billions of tons of sand, cover fertile areas and kill the vegetation they cover. They erode rich soil, wear away humus and leave once productive farms a wasteland.

Wherever dunes appear, certain plants and animals take up residence and live successfully. We may think of dunes as being inhospitable to life, but when we do we are assuming that all living things require a great deal of water, possibly rich humus soil and shade. We could not be more wrong; the dunes thrive with life.

Dunes offer visual beauty and interesting wildlife. The U.S. Congress has helped to assure future preservation of this lovely area along the Lake Michigan shore of Indiana by proclaiming it a National Seashore.

The Birth of a Dune

THE FORCES WHICH form dunes are many. Temperature, wind, mountain ranges and composition of the soil are a few of the inter-relating factors, but luckily these ingredients—in just the right proportions—are comparatively rare. However the misuse of soil by man can bring on a dune growth, and once it is started the build-up of sand may be disastrous to a formerly productive section of country. The dust bowl which developed in the midwestern United States following World War I could have been the start of dunes over some of the richest farm-land in the world. Fortunately soil experts were summoned in time; their planting of cover crops stopped the winds from carrying off the remaining soil before it was too late.

It is generally conceded that the mistake made on these wheatlands was that of forced over-production. Because at the time the United States, with one-sixteenth of the world's productive land area, was attempting to feed one-third of the world, ploughs were worked twenty-four hours a day. Roots were dismembered before they had a chance to bind the soil, and winds carried away the rich powdered humus leaving nothing but sterile sand.

Excavations on the Sahara show that the ancient civilizations of Africa made the same mistake. Deep down under some of the heavy dunes which cover that region there are irrigation ditches, dams and the remains of extensive farmlands which can never be recovered.

Sand dunes—endlessly built up by shifting sands, leveled and built up again elsewhere—provide a unique habitat which, because it is constantly changing, seems endowed with a life of its own. Yet except for some scattered plants and clumps of grass, wasps, scurrying ants and a few well-camouflaged lizards, dunes often seem devoid of most organic life. This is not true, however, for this harsh environment is able to sustain a considerable variety of plant and animal life, specially adapted to the peculiar living conditions of shifting sands. One such animal, the deadly **Russell's viper** (top right), is greatly feared by barefoot walkers from India to Indonesia. Its usual food, however, is frogs, lizards and small birds.

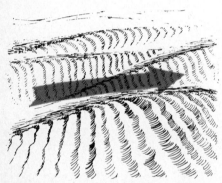

Shape and Speed

A SAND DUNE, either on the coast or inland, has a characteristic shape; prevailing winds blow it into a long slope which rises gently from the place of origin. Winds sweep more sand up this incline until the crest is reached, after which sand drops down in the lee of the dune. As a result of this sudden release of particles, the slope of dunes away from the prevailing wind is steeper than that of the windward side. Because dune building is a never-ending process, these great banks of sand creep relentlessly over the land at speeds of from several inches to several feet or more a year.

The View from the Crest

SOME DUNES MAY BE built up higher than the forests or hills upon which they advance, so that occasionally it is possible to stand on the crest and look over trees or solid terrain below. From this vantage point a sharp dividing line between arid dune vegetation and that of moist forest soil may be visible. As the sand moves on, many years after a forest has been wiped out gaunt dead tree trunks and other objects long buried begin to reappear on the windward slope.

Uncovered by the Wind

DUE TO WIND-CAUSED revelations, sand dunes have long been fruitful hunting grounds for archaeologists in their never-ending search for clues to aid in the assembling of ancient history. Windblown sand, creeping along at varying speeds, covers and eventually uncovers. In this fluid state some ancient artifacts seem almost to float to the top, and as a result an area scoured on one day may voluntarily give up a valuable object on the next.

Sand Casts of Trees

ONE OF THE STRANGEST by-products of the covering and uncovering action of sand dunes are the sand-tree casts found on two channel

Four distinctive **forms of sand dunes** are shown in the drawings at the left. (Top) **Transverse** dunes are formed by moderate one-way winds that move only light sand. (Second) **Longitudinal** dunes are produced by stronger one-way winds that move both fine and coarse sand. (Third) **Barchan** dunes are formed from a relatively small sand supply under the influence of a moderate wind of constant direction. (Bottom) **Star** dunes form in areas where the wind blows from all directions. Unlike other dunes, star dunes remain stationary.

(left)
In some places dunes have formed along the **banks of the Nile.** Despite wind and shifting land, the Egyptian children running up this sloping mound have found a playground.

(right)
On the Sardinian beach shown here, wind and wave action have erected **barrier dunes.** Like the dikes of lowland countries, these dunes help to break the force of heavy waves and tides.

islands, Santa Barbara and Anacapa, near the coastline of California. These tiny bits of land were the homes of three successive cultures of Indians; judging by similar artifacts found on the mainland it is thought that the first of these reigned at about the time of Columbus. Their occupancy was in the midst of a rainy cycle of unknown duration. Before and during this era, great forests of oaklike trees existed; the Indians of that period, seeking shade, built their primitive camps on the roots of the trees.

Drought in the Sequence

THEN CAME DROUGHT, evidently accompanied by terrific winds. For many years the trade-winds blew on the beaches and carried sand, millions of tons of it, to cover and kill the stately oaks. In being killed, however, they were not uprooted but were left standing upright, held in position by the wind-packed particles. How long they remained submerged nobody knows, but in time there was another change in the weather and torrential downpours soaked the dunes to their foundations.

Soon grasses and other plants grew on the rolling hills; and then came land snails—from where or how we do not know. They fed on the new growth and with snail-eating animals non-existent they multiplied unchecked. Eventually, however, their voracious appetites denuded the edible greens. With no food left, the snails perished.

Then the sun and the rains went to work disintegrating the dead snails' shells. During the disintegration, the lime content of the shells was carried underground by the water, where the upright oaks were hidden from sight. The damp, submerged trunks absorbed the water and lime which, combined with sand, made cement which was plastered layer upon layer to the sides of the trees, still deep underground.

Then, in time, the rains became less heavy, and the winds that had enabled the sand to conquer the islands now blew it away. The old dead trees stood revealed. In place of the verdant forest of long ago there was uncovered a forest of cement-like forms in the shapes of trees, thicker than the original trees and hollow in the middle where the wood had rotted away.

Basis for a Calendar

THE TIME OF GROWTH of the trees and the strange chain of events which caused the replicas to form would be pure guesswork, if it were not for the three cultures of Indians who had successively inhabited these islands. Archaeologists know little of the earliest race besides

(above)
Dead, sun-dried branches of trees on the dunes soon become encrusted with **lichens**. These hardy plants withstand severe conditions of heat and dryness.

(right)
This **sandstone tree** was cast by a dune that was drifted by the wind. Perhaps as early as the time of Columbus this tree was covered by sand; then, as the wind again moved the dune, it was exposed.

the fact that their tools of shell and bone are found under the roots of the trees. Time of occupancy of the second culture would also be a rash guess, due to the shifting sand dunes, were it not possible to determine the use of tools also used by mainland cultures. This middle race was known as the Chumash; they in turn were subdued by the Shoshone, a race which maintained possession until bested by the Spaniards. So if we run through this Indian history and correlate it with the sand casts of trees, a fairly accurate calendar may be deduced which places the existence of the living forests, later engulfed by dunes, at a time just prior to America's discovery.

Temperatures by the Inch

P ERHAPS THE MOST dangerous factor encountered in a dune environ- ment is that of heat. Air temperature is not always a good indication of the heat which small crawling animals must withstand. On a clear summer day, if the air temperature on a sea-coast dune is 87° F., the temperature three inches above the sand may be 91°. This temperature increases to 104° one inch above the sand, while the sand surface itself may be as high as 122°! Below the surface the temperature gradually lessens. Some of the temperatures of the dunes of the Mojave, the Sonoran and the Sahara go much higher.

Porous Sand Eliminates Dependency

T HE ABSENCE OF WATER makes dunes fit only for animals which are "specialists". Even when heavy rains do occur, water quickly per- colates down through the loose particles until it is beyond reach of most creatures and sometimes even of deeply penetrating roots. Dunes near bodies of water may hold quantities of the essential fluid but the largest expanses of dune land in the world are far from adequate water supplies. As a result only those plants and animals which have developed adaptations survive. Even in very small dune areas, adapted animals are bound by their instincts to the dry dunes and never venture into the nearby lush vegetation which is, to them, a foreign environment.

(top)
These **sand crabs** are wary of humans. After dark they emerge from their holes to scavenge for food.

(above)
Like some other lizards of the world, this **bobtail lizard** of Australia changes hue as a protective device. It can also regenerate its tail if it is broken off.

Animals Match Their Surroundings

A LTHOUGH THE POLAR REGIONS, the tropics and much of the terrain between have little bearing on sand dunes, a quick perusal of their animals can give us a capsule version of adaptation which should make specialized dune adaptation more meaningful. At both ends of the earth snows are perpetual and the blending hue for snow is white. In the very north and very south this blend is characteristic of animals that are preyed upon as well as for predators.

Now let's come south from the Arctic and pause in the dark forests.

Rabbits, owls, bears, wolves and foxes which had white counterparts are now dark brown and some almost black. This protective blending helps the predator to stalk its prey in dark forest corridors and also helps the prey to escape unnoticed.

Next come the prairie grasslands, green for short periods but more often brown; here the latter hue seemingly controls the region's residents. Let your imagination work for just a moment and in your mind darken or lighten prairie dogs, jack-rabbits or coyotes a shade or two in either direction. Even though the changes are slight, their normally furtive, hard-to-see forms would then become visible.

Farther south we come to the deserts with their sandy, reflective wastes and harsh bright sunlight. Coyotes and jack-rabbits exist here as well, but here even the imagined light ones of the prairie would not be nearly light enough. Some of those on the desert are such a light tan as to be almost white, depending upon the particular region which they call home.

Localized in this tan terrain with its tan animals, we have dunes which are extreme, just as close to white as tan can get. This is where our interest lies and as a graphic illustration the Pinacate volcanic area of Sonora, Mexico, can be our laboratory.

A Desert Laboratory

THE STRANGE PINACATE REGION of about four hundred square miles once steamed with volcanic activity; from the air dozens of craters can be seen at once. Some are small but a few are gigantic, with the floor depressions, 700 feet below, stretching almost half a mile. Many of them are ringed with black lava and form perfect circles. But a few have the symmetry broken by dunes of white sand encroaching over the black and spilling into the now dead cauldrons.

As we approach this wonderland on foot a granite-hued lizard known as the desert iguana suddenly materializes from the granite tone of the ground ahead and scurries off at an unbelievable speed. Most of the

(below, right)
The fast-moving **iguana lizards** live in trees in tropical and desert regions of the Americas. Their diet is made up of the plants they find about them.

(far right)
With its enormous ears, the **fennec** can detect the faint rustlings and squeakings of mice in total darkness at a considerable distance. Better hearing enables an animal to locate more food; this is undoubtedly the evolutionary reason for the huge and efficient ears.

body is gray-white, with a faint dorsal pattern of brown tending to break the form when the creature is motionless. While still walking this typical desert soil, unchanged by either black lava or white sands, we can observe a horned toad with a mottled pattern of brown which slides under a bush and blends as soon as motion is stopped.

Living in the Lava Piles

ANOTHER HUNDRED YARDS toward the outskirts of the volcanic area, blocks of black lava are encountered with increasing frequency. In some places they are in jumbled piles, firmly anchored in the sand but with dark narrow crevices between them. Again there is motion. This time it is a fifteen-inch chuckwalla slithering over the soil, heading for a narrow split in the rock pile. Once there the creature makes no real attempt to hide but instead inflates its lungs with air until its contour matches every indentation of touching rocks. Thus efficiently wedged it is safe from most animals. Only deflation will permit removal.

(top left)
A coat of white fur enables the **polar bear** to blend with a habitat that is perpetually covered with snow and ice.

(top right)
Its varied brown plumage will make it easier for this **owl** to hunt without being seen.

(above, left)
In a dark forest its brown fur may help this **hare** escape its enemies, but it is easily noticed against a background of snow.

(above, right)
Few animals can match the whitish and yellowish tans of sandy deserts better than the **dromedary**, or Arabian camel.

Safety Through Stillness

THIS SHORT WALK over slightly changing ground emphasized the adaptation of hue in a comparatively small area, almost duplicating that which occurs from pole to tropics. There was the iguana with the gray-white background hue and brown dorsal streaks. As long as it maintained immobility it was unseen on the sands that were a blended accumulation of particles of similar tones. Then there was the horned lizard, flattened to the earth so tightly that body shadows did not outline his rocklike form—and there were many flattened rocks on the ground. Next there was the chuckwalla, a desert lizard with a definite affinity for large boulders with crevices available. But desert rocks run the gamut from white to black. As though to take advantage of any situation, chuckwallas are usually two- or three-toned in a pattern which assures a blending of some part of the body.

Almost Black to Match the Lava

LAVA FIELDS are next. Acre after acre of black particles spewed from the tremendous holes which were fashioned when the Pinacate area was a seething inferno. Here, if luck is with the investigator, many of the same creatures found before will be found again. But now the whites are gone and the dark tones predominate, becoming progressively darker as the middle of the lava field is approached. When this imagined point is passed and sights are set on a pure white dune several thousand yards away, scurrying forms may be detected as becoming lighter; when the shifting white sands are reached and penetrated the animals will have become white also.

(below, left)
Large and fierce enough to frighten away most smaller animals, an **eyed lizard** may still have to hide from larger predators. For this, its coloring would best conceal it among grass and green plants. Most lizards match the hue of their surroundings, since those that don't are easy prey and do not live to pass on their unmatched shade to a new generation.

(below, right)
The graceful European **bee-eater** is found from southern Europe and northern Africa to Siberia. Its food is not confined to bees; more than a hundred kinds of insects are possible prey.

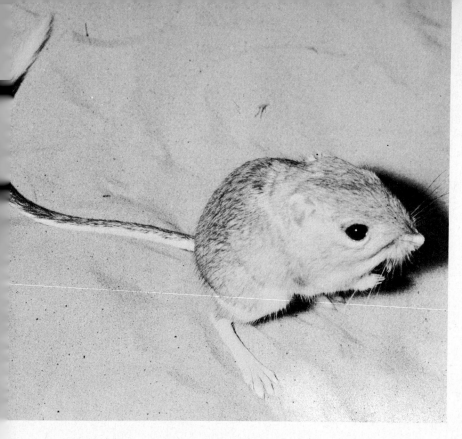

A Matter of Inheritance

THIS MATCHING OF LIFE to terrain is no longer the mystery that it was to primitive peoples. At one time it was held to be the spontaneous work of creation, and this discouraged all need for study and stifled the workings of scientific minds. Then Gregor Johann Mendel, an Austrian monk, let curiosity get the better of existing dogma by promulgating and proving a theory based partially on changes due to inherited characteristics. Other scientists followed his lead and now a wondrous concept of a constantly changing world logically explains much that was not known before.

Changes Due to Predation

LET'S INVESTIGATE these lizards that have reached just the right degree of whiteness by living on the white terrain of the dunes, while those a thousand yards away tend to be black or brown—on black or brown soil. Whether or not these individual reptiles are aware that they are on matching or unmatching soil is unknown, but one in an unmatched situation is quickly seen and eaten by a predatory animal. Thus an unmatched animal may not live long enough to pass on his "unmatchedness" to future generations, while the matched animal's young may be even more matched. So the rules governing inherited characteristics eventually produce animals that match their surroundings.

Aided by its well-developed hind legs, which enable it to jump as much as eight feet, the **kangaroo rat** can move at an astonishing speed. When pursued by a kit fox or a coyote, it can cover twenty feet per second in two-foot hops, and while fleeing it can execute almost a right-angle turn. A nocturnal animal, as its large eyes indicate, it is likely to be found curled up asleep in its burrow during the daylight hours.

Nearly identical in appearance and behavior to the kangaroo rat is the African **jerboa.** It has oversized hind legs, a long tail for balance and large tufted feet.

The Deserts of the World Are Large

IF THE PEOPLE of the world were evenly spaced over the land, one of every seven readers of this book would be a desert resident and most of these desert dwellers would have dunes within a relatively short distance of their homes. That deserts occupy so much surface of the earth might seem to be an exaggeration, but let's look at the facts.

Australia—world's largest island, or smallest continent—has only a narrow coastal belt suitable for livelihood by most standards. The entire interior is a region of scanty rainfall, with extreme heat during the day and extreme cold at night. The Sahara, home of nomads and camels, is much larger than is generally supposed. Its desert area, classified by rainfall and lack of humidity, is larger than the entire United States. Deserts of western North America, the Chihuahuan, the Sonoran, the Mojave and the Colorado look small on maps, and with the well-engineered highways of today are no longer a real threat to transport. In pioneer days, however, this was not so, for their thousands of square miles were the greatest barrier to early cross-country travel.

The Conquest of Deserts by Humans

EVEN AS LATE as the 1920s a corduroy, or plank road, was used to cross the dunes near Yuma. This was an ingenious device made up of planks ten or twelve feet long set crosswise to the line of travel. Each plank was wired to the next one with a space of an inch or so between. This gave flexibility, and the jogging of the early cars had a tendency to make the novel roadbed float on top of the shifting dunes.

Extreme winds, however, would often cause drifts to cover some portions. But, as was customary in those days, crowbars were a necessary part of a car repair kit. Careful prying would let the sand settle through the cracks and bring the road to the surface once again. Contemporary inventiveness, or possibly copying by humans, brought similar roads to various sand dune regions of the world. Some are still in use.

Dune Conquest by the Lower Animals

Inventiveness or copying, however, cannot be used to explain the strange phenomenon which places animals that are unrelated but of similar appearance on various deserts of the world remotely situated each from the other. In the dune country of the Sonoran, Mojave and Colorado deserts, there is a small rattler known as the sidewinder. As might be expected, this reptile is light, so light in fact that if it were placed on normal dirt a white ribbon appearance would be the result. But this creature has gone far beyond mere protective marking. Throughout the ages, its life on shifting sands has even affected its mode of travel. As the name sidewinder implies, it moves with a broadside motion, leaving a series of disconnected parallel impressions by progressively arching its body off the ground and replacing the loops six or seven inches away.

The chief prey of the sidewinder are kangaroo rats, which are yellowwhite animals with short front and long hind legs. The hind feet have furry growths around the toes which, in a way, are snowshoes for the powdery sands of the dunes. They use their long tufted tails for balance when making their bounding jumps to escape a sidewinder. But, believe it or not, this identical act with different actors can be seen on the distant stage of the far-off Sahara.

Similarities in Distant Places

On this Egyptian desert there is a facsimile of the sidewinder called the Sahara viper, and it feeds on what externally is almost a perfect duplicate of a kangaroo rat, known as the jerboa. So here

(above)
Since much of Australia is arid, reptiles found there, such as this **half-ringed snake,** have the ability to live in harsh surroundings. In general, desert snakes are adapted to wriggle into and through loose sand.

(left)
The eyes of the African **puff adder** are protected from sand by the clear shields that cover them. When in danger these vipers are able to bury themselves in the sand. In this picture, a young adder follows its parent.

we have a strange situation: four totally unrelated creatures broken into antagonistic pairs and living on deserts thousands of miles apart. The two reptiles are in no way related, and neither are the two mammals, hence similarity of looks, habits or specialized locomotion cannot be answered by family relationships.

An explanation of how these creatures developed should start with the premise that nature abhors a vacuum. Early in the earth's history, when deserts and, later, sand dunes began to dot some sections of the world they were inhospitable places. Life as it was then was ill-equipped to contend with the hardships imposed by such regions.

Gradual Changes

Bᴜᴛ ᴀᴍᴏɴɢꜱᴛ ᴛʜᴇ ᴀɴɪᴍᴀʟꜱ there were some crowding the borders of the sandy wastes. The first changes making a life on sand possible were probably based on hue. But there were also water conservation, avoidance of killing heat, better traction on shifting sands and dozens of other infinitesimal refinements about which we still know almost nothing. Occasionally in the mass of offspring born through thousands of years, one would be born slightly different from the others. If the difference had survival value it would be passed on to future generations, permitting a deeper penetration into the sandy wastes,

(above)
This engaging **curly-tailed lizard** is quite at home in shifting sand; its long toes enable it to run about at will. Why it carries its tail in this manner is unknown, but it may be for balance. These lizards are so tame they will eat fruit from a person's fingers.

(left)
Native to Australia, this large, **blue-tongued lizard** is one of the family of skinks. The female bears alive from ten to fifteen young at a time.

(far left)
Banded geckos have eyelids, features that are absent in most geckos. The name "gecko" is based on the call and is a near-imitation of the sound. The young of this species emerge from the egg after several months of incubation.

and in time the animals conquered the dunes. Rats had their front feet shrink, their hind legs lengthen, and grew tufts of fur spreading from their soles to prevent sinking in the sand. Thus kangaroo rats as we know them now came into being.

While nature's striving for perfection of species suitable for living on specialized terrain was taking place on the deserts of North America, the same forces of development were also at work in Africa and Australia. Through slow trial and error, mistakes were eliminated and

The **field vole**, *Microtus*, is a common inhabitant of many dunes. It constructs nests from grass under protecting objects lying on the sand. Bits of grass from its food gathering may be seen on the sand in this picture.

advantages—no matter how slight—passed on to offspring. As a result of this convergence toward a peak of efficient performance there are marsupial rats in Australia, jerboas in Africa and kangaroo rats in North America. All three look and act much alike.

Proofs Are Many

THERE ARE MANY OTHER examples of convergent evolution on the continents of the world. Some of those which occur on deserts might be listed and paired as follows: horned toad (North America) and moloch (Australia); kit fox (North America) and fennec (Africa); sidewinder (North America) and Sahara viper (Africa); kangaroo rat (North America), jerboa (Sahara) and marsupial rat (Australia). Even some desert plants have undergone ages of convergent evolution and independently attained remarkable similarities. Cactuses, for instance, are confined exclusively to North and South America, and if broad popular characteristics were listed they would be green plants with waxy skins, usually leafless and often armoured with sharp spines. The deserts of Australia and Africa have plants which exactly fit that same description. But despite the similarity there is no relationship between these look-alike growths.

Continued in Volume 6

CREDITS
Color photographs and illustrations appearing in this volume were supplied by the following: Photo Researchers, Inc.; The American Museum of Natural History; Armando Curcio; Doubleday & Company, Inc.; U.S. Department of the Interior, National Park Service; and H. S. Stuttman Co., Inc.

Cover illustration and illustration on page 537 were photographed at The American Museum of Natural History.